Revise for Higher Mathematics

John Dalton   Carole Ford
Jim Pennel   Tom Sanaghan

About this book

This book is designed to help you achieve the best possible grade in the Higher Mathematics examination.

Revise for Higher Mathematics covers key topics which are tested in the Higher. You can use it to help you revise at the end of a unit or of the course, or use it throughout the course alongside the course textbook: *Heinemann Higher Mathematics* which provides complete coverage of the new Higher syllabus.

Each question in the book is labelled **U** or **C** to indicate whether that question is at unit level or course level.

Helping you prepare for your exam

To help you prepare, each topic offers you:

Key points to remember – these summarize the mathematical ideas you need to know and be able to use.

Worked examples and examination questions – help you understand and remember important methods, and show you how to set out your answers clearly.

Revision exercises – help you practice using important methods to solve problems. Past paper questions are included so you can be sure you are reaching the right standard, and answers are given at the back of the book so you can assess your progress.

Test yourself questions – help you see where you need extra revision and practice. If you do need extra help they show you where to look in the *Heinemann Higher Mathematics* textbook.

Assessment practice and advice on revising

Assessment practice papers – these papers at the end of the book provide a set of questions of examination standard. They give you an opportunity to practice assessments before you meet the real thing. Non-calculator papers are included.

How to revise – For advice on revising before the exam read the **How to revise** section on the following pages.

How to revise using this book

Making the best use of your revision time

The chapters in this book are arranged to match the order of the Higher units so you can work your way through them from beginning to end. But **how** you work on them depends on how much time there is between now and your examination.

If you are revising for a unit test you may wish to work through only the unit questions (marked **U**) and the specimen unit assessments.

If you are revising for the course examination then you can work through each topic in turn, covering the key points and worked examples before doing the revision exercises and test yourself questions. You can then use the specimen course assessments as a final practice.

Using the test yourself sections

Each test yourself section provides a set of key questions. Try each question:

- If you can do it and obtain the correct answer than move on to the next topic. Come back to this topic later to consolidate your knowledge and understanding by working through the key points, worked examples and revision exercises.
- If you cannot do the question, or get an incorrect answer or part answer then read through the suggested pages of Heinemann Higher Mathematics before trying the test yourself questions again. If you need more help, look back to the worked examples at the beginning of the chapter.

Reviewing the key points

Most of the key points are straightforward ideas that you should know and understand. Imagine explaining each idea to a friend in your own words, and say it out loud as you do so. This is a better way of making ideas stick than just reading them silently from the page.

As you work through the book, remember to go back over key points from earlier topics at least once a week. This will help you to remember them in the exam.

Working on the worked examples

Read the question at the start of each worked example and think about what it is asking you to do. Try to work out which key point(s) you need to use, and how to answer the question before you look at the answer itself.

Follow the working through carefully, making sure you understand each stage.

Using the revision exercises

Tackle the revision exercises in the same way as the worked examples. If you need to, go back to the key points and worked examples to see which method to use.

If you are not sure what to do, look at the answer at the back of the book to see if this gives you a clue.

- If the marker understands that you have the right method you may gain some marks even if you make an error in a calculation.

The specimen assessments

Use the unit and course assessments as a final preparation. The worked solutions should assist with any areas of difficulty.

When sitting assessments **read the questions carefully**. Many candidates lose marks because they haven't done this. Check that you give the answer required.

- Show all stages in your working. If a question carries several marks then most of them will be for the method used to obtain the answer.

The final examination

The key to success in the Higher is practice in answering the questions. Spend time in the weeks leading to the exam tackling all the questions you have access to, including specimen and past papers.

1 The straight line

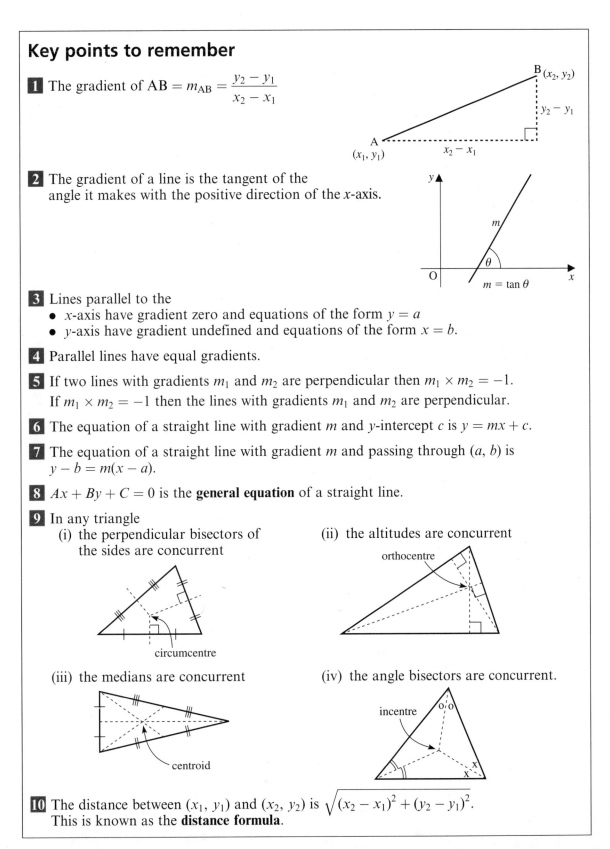

Key points to remember

1 The gradient of $AB = m_{AB} = \dfrac{y_2 - y_1}{x_2 - x_1}$

2 The gradient of a line is the tangent of the angle it makes with the positive direction of the x-axis.

$m = \tan \theta$

3 Lines parallel to the
  - x-axis have gradient zero and equations of the form $y = a$
  - y-axis have gradient undefined and equations of the form $x = b$.

4 Parallel lines have equal gradients.

5 If two lines with gradients m_1 and m_2 are perpendicular then $m_1 \times m_2 = -1$.
If $m_1 \times m_2 = -1$ then the lines with gradients m_1 and m_2 are perpendicular.

6 The equation of a straight line with gradient m and y-intercept c is $y = mx + c$.

7 The equation of a straight line with gradient m and passing through (a, b) is
$y - b = m(x - a)$.

8 $Ax + By + C = 0$ is the **general equation** of a straight line.

9 In any triangle
  (i) the perpendicular bisectors of the sides are concurrent

circumcentre

  (ii) the altitudes are concurrent

orthocentre

  (iii) the medians are concurrent

centroid

  (iv) the angle bisectors are concurrent.

incentre

10 The distance between (x_1, y_1) and (x_2, y_2) is $\sqrt{(x_2 - x_1)^2 + (y_2 - y_1)^2}$.
This is known as the **distance formula**.

U Example 1

A line passes through the points P(−2, 5) and Q(1, −1).
Find the equation of this line.

Solution

$$m_{PQ} = \frac{-1-5}{1-(-2)} = \frac{-6}{3} = -2$$

Equation of PQ is $y - b = m(x - a)$
$$y - 5 = -2(x - (-2))$$
$$y - 5 = -2x - 4$$
$$2x + y - 1 = 0$$

U Example 2

A line passes through an angle of 72° with the positive direction of the x-axis.
Find the gradient of the line.

Solution

Gradient of line, $m = \tan 72° = 3.1$

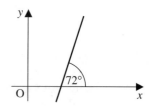

U Example 3

(a) The line AB is parallel to a line with equation $5x - y - 2 = 0$. Write down the gradient of AB.

(b) The line PQ is perpendicular to a line with equation $5x - y - 2 = 0$. Write down the gradient of PQ.

Solution

(a) $5x - y - 2 = 0$

$y = 5x - 2$

$m_{AB} = 5$

(b) $m_{AB} = 5$

$$m_{PQ} = \frac{-1}{5}$$

C Example 4

Find the equation of the perpendicular bisector
of the line joining P(-5, -2) and Q(13, 4).

Solution

$$m_{PQ} = \frac{4 - (-2)}{13 - (-5)} = \frac{6}{18} = \frac{1}{3}$$

$$m_{\text{perp. bis.}} = -3$$

Mid-point of PQ is M$\left(\dfrac{-5 + 13}{2}, \dfrac{-2 + 4}{2}\right)$

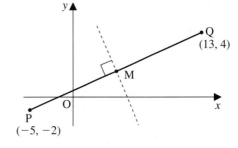

The perpendicular bisector passes through
M(4, 1).

Equation of perpendicular bisector is

$$y - b = m(x - a)$$
$$y - 1 = -3(x - 4)$$
$$y + 3x - 13 = 0$$

C Example 5

AB has equation $x - y - 2 = 0$.
CB has equation $x + 2y - 18 = 0$.
Calculate the size of angle ABC.

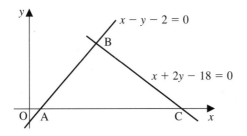

Solution

For line AB: $x - y - 2 = 0$

$$y = x - 2$$
$$m_{AB} = 1$$
$$\tan xAB = 1$$
angle CAB $= 45°$

For line CB: $x + 2y - 18 = 0$

$$y = -\tfrac{1}{2}x + 9$$
$$m_{CB} = -\tfrac{1}{2}$$
$$\tan xCB = -0.5$$
angle $xCB = 153.4°$
So angle ACB $= 26.6°$

Hence angle ABC $= 108.4°$

C Example 6

Triangle ABC has vertices A(3, 0), B(−12, 9) and C(0, −3).
(a) Show that triangle ABC is right-angled at C.
(b) Find the equation of median AD.
(c) Find the equation of the altitude CE.
(d) Find the point of intersection of AD and CE.

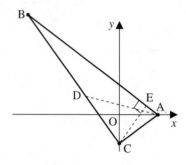

Solution

(a) $m_{AC} = \dfrac{-3 - 0}{0 - 3} = \dfrac{-3}{-3} = 1$

$m_{BC} = \dfrac{-3 - 9}{0 - (-12)} = \dfrac{-12}{12} = -1$

$m_{AC} \times m_{BC} = -1$

AC is perpendicular to BC, therefore triangle ABC is right-angled at C.

(b) The mid-point of BC is D(−6, 3).

$m_{AD} = \dfrac{3 - 0}{-6 - 3} = \dfrac{3}{-9} = \dfrac{-1}{3}$

The equation of AD is $y - 0 = \dfrac{-1}{3}(x - 3)$

$$3y = -x + 3$$
$$x + 3y = 3$$

(c) $m_{AB} = \dfrac{9 - 0}{-12 - 3} = \dfrac{9}{-15} = \dfrac{-3}{5}$

$m_{CE} = \dfrac{5}{3}$

The equation of CE is $y - (-3) = \dfrac{5}{3}(x - 0)$

$$3y + 9 = 5x$$
$$5x - 3y = 9$$

(d) AD and CE meet where $x + 3y = 3$
and $5x - 3y = 9$

Solve these equations simultaneously to give

$x = 2$

$y = \frac{1}{3}$

The point of intersection of AD and CE is $\left(2, \frac{1}{3}\right)$.

Revision exercise 1

U 1 Find the gradients of the lines joining:
(a) A(4, 4) and B(6, 7)
(b) M(1, −3) and N(8, −4)

U 2 Quadrilateral PQRS has coordinates P(5, 3), Q(−4, 1), R(−3, −3) and S(6, −1).
(a) Find the gradient of each side of PQRS.
(b) Name the type of quadrilateral.

U   3   Find the angle that the line joining each pair of points makes
with the positive direction of the *x*-axis.
(a) A(7, 6) and B(−1, −2)
(b) R(11, 6) and S(−3, −4)
(c) T(−9, 7) and U(−7, −6)
(d) K(−3, 2) and L(10, −3)

U   4   Find the gradient of each line.

(a)   (b)

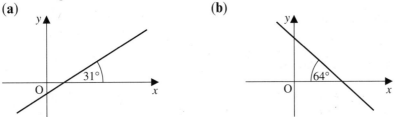

U   5   A line GH has gradient $\frac{-2}{3}$. It crosses the *x*-axis at G(5, 0)
and the *y*-axis at H.
Calculate the acute angle that GH makes with the *y*-axis.

U   6   Find the gradients of lines that are (i) parallel to and
(ii) perpendicular to:
(a) $y = 2x + 5$ (b) $y = -\frac{1}{2}x + 1$ (c) $x + y - 3 = 0$
(d) $x + 4y - 3 = 0$ (e) $5x - 2y = 1$ (f) $4y - 3x + 7 = 0$

U   7   Find the equation of the line through the given point and
with the given gradient:
(a) (2, 1), 3   (b) (3, −6), −4   (c) (0, −4), $-\frac{1}{4}$

U   8   Find the equation of the line:
(a) through (6, 1) and parallel to $y = 4x - 8$
(b) through (−9, 2) and perpendicular to $x + y = 7$
(c) perpendicular to $3x + y = -6$ and passing through the
origin.

C   9   Show that AB and BC are perpendicular.

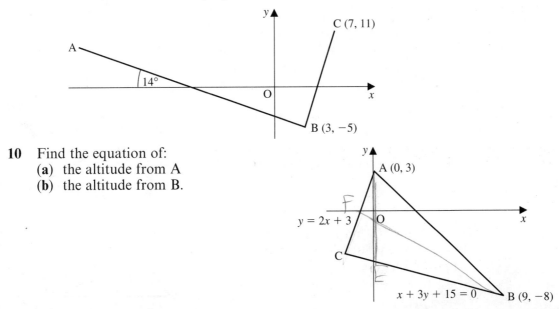

C   10   Find the equation of:
(a) the altitude from A
(b) the altitude from B.

C 11 Find the equation of the altitude from P for a triangle with vertices:
(a) P(4, −2), Q(−3, −1) and R(1, 3)
(b) P(4, 0), C(0, −5) and D(2, 5)

C 12 Find the equations of all the altitudes of the triangle with vertices K(7, 8), L(6, 2) and M(−5, 2).

C 13 Find the equation of the median from A for a triangle with vertices:
(a) A(3, 4), B(−4, −1) and C(6, −3)
(b) A(−6, 6), G(1, −4) and H(11, −2)

C 14 (a) Find the equations of all three medians of the triangle with vertices R(2, 6), S(8, −4) and T(−2, −4).
(b) Prove the medians are concurrent.

C 15 Rhombus PQRS has vertices P(3, 8), Q(4, 1), R(−1, −4) and S(−2, 3).
(a) Find the equations of the diagonals of PQRS.
(b) Find the point of intersection of the diagonals.

C 16 F(1, 7), G(11, −3) and H(2, −6) are the vertices of triangle FGH.
The median from H meets FG at P and the altitude from F meets HG at Q.
Find the coordinates of the point of intersection of HP and FQ.

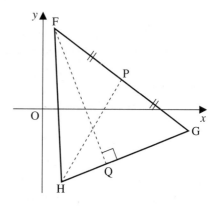

C 17 Triangle ABC has vertices A(−2, 6), B(−5, −4) and C(5, 0).
(a) Find the equation of AM, the median from A.
(b) Find the equation of BP, the altitude from B.
(c) Find the x-coordinate of Q, the point of intersection of AM and BP.

C 18 Triangle ABC has vertices A(−3, −3), B(−1, 1) and C(7, −3).
(a) Show that triangle ABC is right-angled at B.

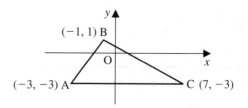

(b) The medians AD and BE intersect at M.
(i) Find the equations of AD and BE.
(ii) Hence find the coordinates of M.
[Higher]

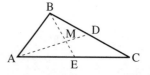

Test yourself	What to review
	If your answer is incorrect:
U 1 (a) Find the gradient of the line joining K(5, −1) and L(−1, 7). (b) Find the size of the angle that KL makes with the positive direction of the *x*-axis.	*Review Heinemann Higher Mathematics Chapter 1, pages 1 to 3*
U 2 If R is the point (8, 2) and S is the point (−2, 4), find the equation of a line perpendicular to RS and passing through R.	*Review Heinemann Higher Mathematics Chapter 1, pages 10 and 11*
U 3 Find the equation of the line passing through the point (2, −3) and parallel to the line with equation $x + 2y = 6$.	*Review Heinemann Higher Mathematics Chapter 1, pages 10 and 11*
C 4 Triangle HRC has coordinates H(3, 5) R(7, −7) and C(−15, −1). Show that triangle HRC is right-angled and name the right angle.	*Review Heinemann Higher Mathematics Chapter 1, pages 5 to 7*
C 5 Triangle ABC has vertices A(2, 0), B(10, −12) and C(−18, 2). Find the coordinates of the point where the median from C meets the perpendicular bisector of CB.	*Review Heinemann Higher Mathematics Chapter 1, pages 14 to 17*

Test yourself answers

1 (a) $\dfrac{-4}{3}$ (b) 126.9°   **2** $5x - y - 38 = 0$ **3** $x + 2y + 4 = 0$ **4** angle CHR   **5** (−3, −3)

2 Sets and functions

Key points to remember

1 A **function** or mapping from a set A to a set B is a rule that relates each element in set A to one and only one element in set B.
The set of elements in set A is called the **domain**.
The set of images in set B is called the **range**.

2 A composite function can be written in the form $h(x) = g(f(x))$ and is read as 'g of f of x'.

3 In general $f(g(x)) \neq g(f(x))$

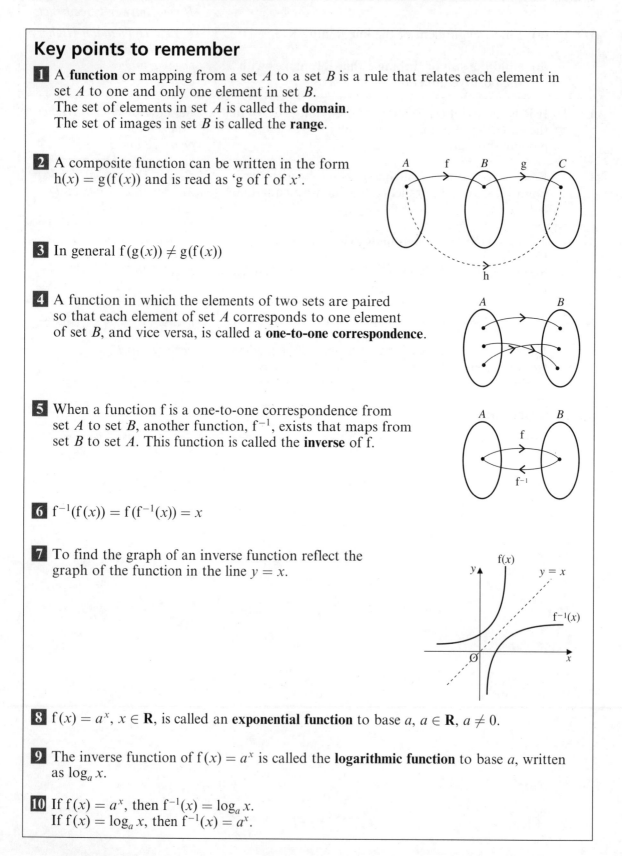

4 A function in which the elements of two sets are paired so that each element of set A corresponds to one element of set B, and vice versa, is called a **one-to-one correspondence**.

5 When a function f is a one-to-one correspondence from set A to set B, another function, f^{-1}, exists that maps from set B to set A. This function is called the **inverse** of f.

6 $f^{-1}(f(x)) = f(f^{-1}(x)) = x$

7 To find the graph of an inverse function reflect the graph of the function in the line $y = x$.

8 $f(x) = a^x$, $x \in \mathbf{R}$, is called an **exponential function** to base a, $a \in \mathbf{R}$, $a \neq 0$.

9 The inverse function of $f(x) = a^x$ is called the **logarithmic function** to base a, written as $\log_a x$.

10 If $f(x) = a^x$, then $f^{-1}(x) = \log_a x$.
If $f(x) = \log_a x$, then $f^{-1}(x) = a^x$.

Outcome 2

Associate functions and graphs.
See Chapters 3 and 4 for other functions and graphs.

Performance criteria

PC(b)   Sketch and identify exponential and logarithmic graphs.
PC(c)   Find composite functions of the form $f(g(x))$, given $f(x)$ and $g(x)$.

U   Example 1

The graph of $y = 2^x$ is shown in the diagram below.
(a) Write down the equation of the graph of the exponential
     function of the form $y = a^x$ which passes through the point
     (1, 5) as shown in the diagram.
(b) On a similar diagram, draw the graph of the function
     $y = 4^x$.

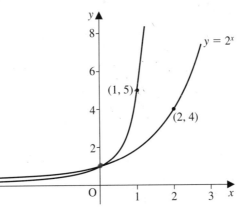

Solution

(a) For the function $y = a^x$, when $x = 1$ and $y = 5$ then $5 = a^1$.
     So $a = 5$ and the equation of the graph is $y = 5^x$.

(b) $y = 4^x$

x	0	1	2
y	1	4	16

U Example 2

The diagram below shows part of the graph of a logarithmic function.

(a) Write down the equation of the function.

(b) Make a copy of the diagram and on it draw the graph of the function $y = \log_5 x$, showing clearly where it crosses the x-axis and marking in the coordinates of one other point that it passes through.

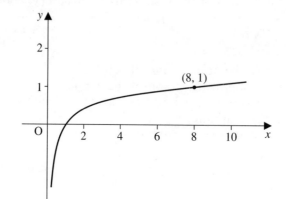

Solution

(a) $y = \log_8 x$

(b)

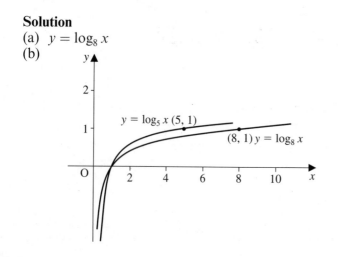

U Example 3

(a) Two functions f and g are given by $f(x) = -2x^2$ and $g(x) = 5 - 3x$. Obtain an expression for $f(g(x))$ and for $g(f(x))$.

(b) Functions h and k, defined on suitable domains, are given by $h(x) = 5x$ and $k(x) = \cos x°$. Find $k(h(x))$ and $h(k(x))$.

Solution

(a) $f(g(x)) = f(5 - 3x)$
$= -2(5 - 3x)^2$
$= -50 + 60x - 18x^2$

$g(f(x)) = g(-2x^2)$
$= 5 - 3(-2x^2)$
$= 5 + 6x^2$

(b) $k(h(x)) = k(5x)$
$= \cos 5x°$

$h(k(x)) = h(\cos x°)$
$= 5\cos x°$

C **Example 4**

A function f is defined by $f(x) = 2x + 3$ where $x \in \mathbf{R}$ and a second function g is defined by $g(x) = \dfrac{x^2 + 25}{x^2 - 25}$ where $x \in \mathbf{R}$, $x \neq \pm 5$.

The function H is defined by $H(x) = g(f(x))$. For which real values of x is the function H undefined? [Higher]

Solution

$$H(x) = g(f(x)) = g(2x + 3)$$

$$= \frac{(2x + 3)^2 + 25}{(2x + 3)^2 - 25}$$

$$= \frac{4x^2 + 12x + 9 + 25}{4x^2 + 12x + 9 - 25}$$

$$= \frac{4x^2 + 12x + 34}{4x^2 + 12x - 16}$$

$$= \frac{2(2x^2 + 6x + 17)}{4(x + 4)(x - 1)}$$

The function H is undefined when the denominator is zero. Hence, the function is undefined for $x = -4$ and $x = 1$.

Revision exercise 2

U **1** The graph of $y = 3^x$ is shown in the diagram.
(a) Write down the equation of the graph of the exponential function $y = a^x$, which passes through the point (1, 10) as shown in the diagram.
(b) On a similar diagram, draw the graph of the function $y = 6^x$.

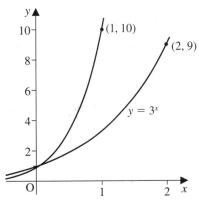

U **2** (a) Draw the graph of the function $y = 8^x$.
(b) The point $(a, \frac{1}{64})$ lies on the graph of $y = 8^x$. Find the value of a.

U **3** The diagram shows part of the graph of a logarithmic function.
(a) Write down the equation of the function.
(b) Make a copy of the diagram and on it draw the graph of the function $y = \log_6 x$, showing clearly where it crosses the x-axis and marking in the coordinates of one other point that it passes through.

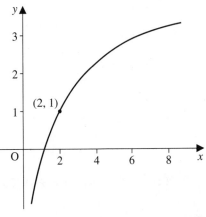

U **4** Draw the graph of the function $y = \log_3 x$, showing clearly where it crosses the x-axis and marking in the coordinates of one other point that lies on the graph.

U **5** Functions f and g are defined on the set R with $f(x) = 3x - 1$ and $g(x) = 2x$.
  (a) Evaluate (i) $g(f(1))$ and (ii) $g(f(-3))$.
  (b) State a formula for $g(f(x))$.

U **6** For each pair of functions write a formula for $f(g(x))$.
  (a) $f(x) = x + 5$, $g(x) = x^2$ (b) $f(x) = x^3$, $g(x) = x + 2$
  (c) $f(x) = 3x$, $g(x) = \cos x$ (d) $f(x) = 3^x$, $g(x) = x - 2$

U **7** For each pair of functions in question **6** write a formula for $g(f(x))$.

U **8** (a) Draw the graph of the function $f(x) = 4^x$ for $-2 \leqslant x \leqslant 2$ and on the same diagram sketch its inverse.
  (b) State the inverse function.

U **9** (a) Draw the graph of the function $f(x) = \log_7 x$ for $0 < x < 10$ and on the same diagram sketch its inverse.
  (b) State the inverse function.

U **10** Functions k and h are defined on the set of real numbers by $k(x) = \dfrac{2x - 5}{3}$ and $h(x) = \dfrac{3x + 5}{2}$. Find $k(h(x))$. What can you say about functions k and h?

C **11** Draw the graph of each function and on the same diagram sketch its inverse.
  (a) $f(x) = 3x$ (b) $f(x) = \frac{1}{2}x - 5$ (c) $f(x) = x^3 + 5$

C **12** The functions f and g, defined on a suitable domain, are given by $f(x) = \dfrac{1}{x^2 - 16}$ and $g(x) = x - 3$.
  (a) Find $k(x) = f(g(x))$ in its simplest form.
  (b) State a suitable domain for k.

C **13** The functions f and g are defined on a suitable domain by $f(x) = x^2 - 1$ and $g(x) = x^2 + 2$.
  (a) Find an expression for $f(g(x))$.
  (b) Factorise $f(g(x))$.   [Higher]

C **14** Functions f and g are defined on the set of real numbers by $f(x) = x - 1$ and $g(x) = x^2$.
  (a) Find formulae for (i) $f(g(x))$ and (ii) $g(f(x))$.
  (b) The function h is defined by $h(x) = f(g(x)) + g(f(x))$. Show that $h(x) = 2x^2 - 2x$ and sketch the graph of h.
                                    [Higher]

Test yourself	**What to review**

If your answer is incorrect:

U 1 The graph of $y = 5^x$ is shown in the diagram below.
   (a) Write down the equation of the graph of the exponential function of the form $y = a^x$ which passes through the point (1, 9) as shown in the diagram.
   (b) On a similar diagram, draw the graph of the function $y = 7^x$.

Review Heinemann Higher Mathematics Chapter 2, page 30

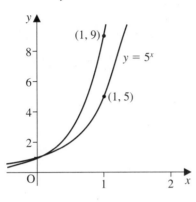

U 2 The diagram below shows part of the graph of a logarithmic function.
   (a) Write down the equation of the function.
   (b) Make a copy of the diagram and on it draw the graph of the function $y = \log_9 x$, showing clearly where it crosses the x-axis and marking in the coordinates of one other point that it passes through.

Review Heinemann Higher Mathematics Chapter 2, page 31

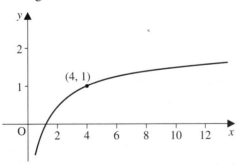

U 3 (a) Two functions f and g are given by $f(x) = 4x^2$ and $g(x) = 4 - 2x$.
   Obtain an expression for $f(g(x))$.
   (b) Functions h and k, defined on suitable domains, are given by $h(x) = 7x$ and $k(x) = \tan x°$. Find $k(h(x))$.

Review Heinemann Higher Mathematics Chapter 2, pages 25 to 27

U 4 Draw the graph of the function $f(x) = 2^x$ for $-2 \leqslant x \leqslant 3$ and on the same diagram sketch $f^{-1}(x)$.

Review Heinemann Higher Mathematics Chapter 2, pages 27 to 32

C 5 Functions f and g are defined on the set of real numbers by $f(x) = \dfrac{x}{2+x}$, $x \neq -2$ and $g(x) = 2x - 1$.

Review Heinemann Higher Mathematics Chapter 2, pages 25 to 27

(a) Find $f(g(x))$.
(b) Find $f(f(x))$.
(c) State suitable domains for (i) $f(g(x))$ and (ii) $f(f(x))$.

Test yourself answers

1 (a) $y = 9^x$ (b)

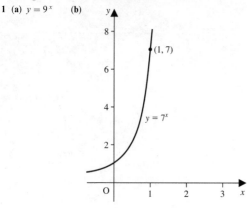

2 (a) $y = \log_4 x$ (b)

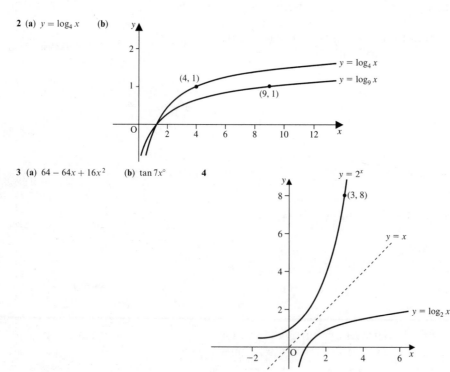

3 (a) $64 - 64x + 16x^2$ (b) $\tan 7x°$ 4

5 (a) $\dfrac{2x-1}{2x+1}$ (b) $\dfrac{x}{4+3x}$ (c) (i) $x \in \mathbf{R}$, $x \neq -\frac{1}{2}$ (ii) $x \in \mathbf{R}$, $x \neq -\frac{4}{3}$

3 Graphs of functions

Key points to remember

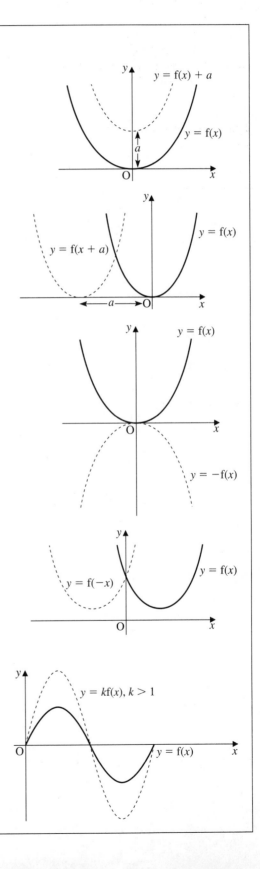

1 To obtain the graph of $y = f(x) + a$,
slide $y = f(x)$ **vertically**

    upwards for $a > 0$
downwards for $a < 0$.

2 To obtain the graph of $y = f(x + a)$,
slide $y = f(x)$ **horizontally**

    to the left for $a > 0$
to the right for $a < 0$.

3 To obtain the graph of $y = -f(x)$,
reflect $y = f(x)$ **in the x-axis**.

4 To obtain the graph of $y = f(-x)$,
reflect $y = f(x)$ **in the y-axis**.

5 To obtain the graph of $y = kf(x)$,
stretch or **compress** $y = f(x)$
vertically by a factor of k:

    stretch for $k > 1$
compress for $k < 1$.

6 To obtain the graph of $y = f(kx)$,
stretch or **compress** $y = f(x)$
horizontally by a factor of k:

compress for $k > 1$
    stretch for $k < 1$.

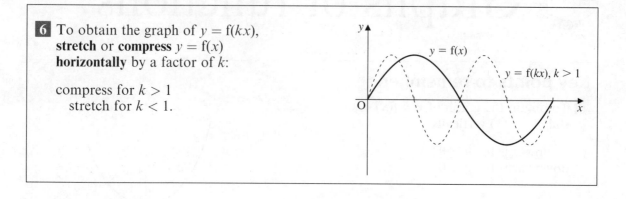

Outcome 2

Associate functions and graphs.
See Chapters 2 and 4 for other functions and graphs.

Performance criteria

PC(a)   Sketch and identify related graphs and functions.

U   Example 1

The diagram shows part of the graph of $y = f(x)$.
(a) Make a sketch of $y = f(x)$ and on the
same diagram draw the graph of
$y = f(x + 3)$.
(b) Make a second sketch of $y = f(x)$ and on
the same diagram draw the graph of
$y = 2f(x)$.

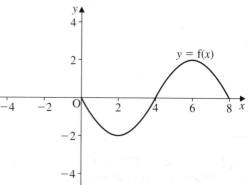

Solution

(a) Slide the graph horizontally
3 units to the left

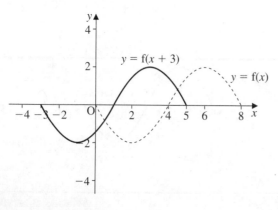

(b) Stretch the graph
vertically by a factor of 2

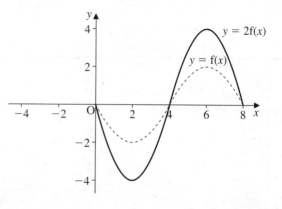

U Example 2

(a) The diagram shows part of the graph
of $y = f(x)$ and, shown by a dotted curve,
the graph of a related function.
Write down an equation for the
related function.

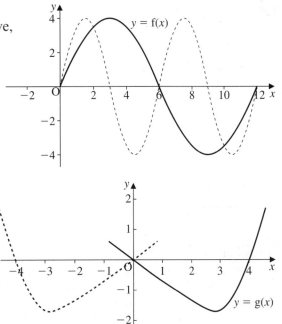

(b) The diagram shows part of the
graph of $y = g(x)$ and, shown by
a dotted curve, the graph of a
related function.
Write down an equation for the
related function.

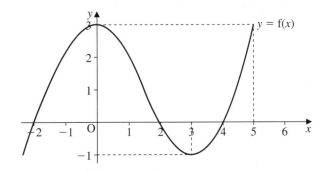

Solution

(a) $y = f(x)$ is compressed by a factor of 2 so the related
function is $y = f(2x)$.
(b) $y = g(x)$ is reflected in the y-axis so the related function is
$y = g(-x)$.

C Example 3

The diagram shows part of the graph
of $y = f(x)$.
Sketch the graph of $y = 1 - f(x)$.

Solution

Sketch $y = -f(x)$ by reflecting $y = f(x)$ in the x-axis. Slide up
1 unit to give $y = 1 - f(x)$.

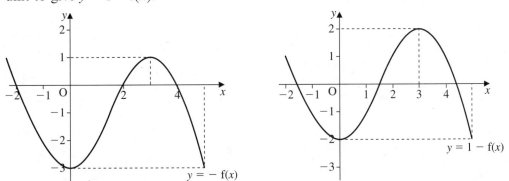

C Example 4

The diagram shows part of
the graph of a function of the
form $y = \log_a (x - b)$.
Find the values of a and b

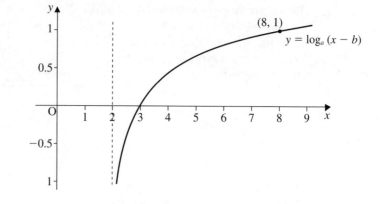

Solution

Since the graph passes through (3, 0) the graph of $y = \log_a x$ has
been moved horizontally to the right by 2 units. So $b = 2$.
The point (8, 1) is 2 units to the right of (6, 1) so $y = \log_a x$
passes through (6, 1).
Hence $a = 6$.
The graph of the function is therefore $y = \log_6 (x - 2)$.

Revision exercise 3

U 1 Part of the graph of $y = f(x)$ is shown.
Also shown are the graphs of two related
functions. Find the values of k and n.

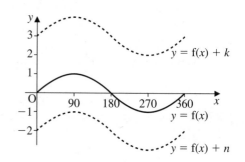

U 2 Part of the graph of $y = f(x)$ is shown.
(**a**) Copy the graph and on the same
diagram sketch graphs of the
related functions $y = f(x) + 2$ and
$y = f(x) - 3$.
(**b**) Annotate both sketches with the
images of the points A, B, C and
D, and give their coordinates.

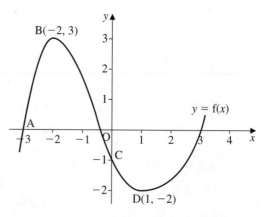

U 3 Part of the graph of $y = f(x)$ is shown. Also shown are the
graphs of two related functions.
Find the values of k and n.

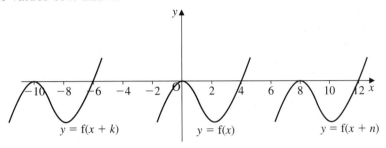

$y = f(x + k)$ $y = f(x)$ $y = f(x + n)$

U 4 Part of the graph of $y = f(x)$ is
shown.
  (a) Copy the graph and on the
same diagram sketch graphs
of the related functions
$y = f(x - 6)$ and
$y = f(x + 1)$.
  (b) Annotate both sketches
with the images of the
points A, B, C and D, and
give their coordinates.

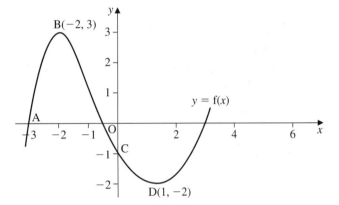

U 5 Part of the graph of $y = f(x)$ is
shown.
  (a) Copy the graph and on the
same diagram sketch a
graph of the related
function $y = -f(x)$.
  (b) Annotate the sketch with
the images of the points
A, B, C and D, and give
their coordinates.

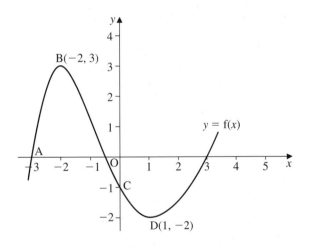

U 6 Part of the graph of $y = k(x)$ is shown.
Copy the graph and on the same diagram
sketch the graph of $y = -k(x)$.

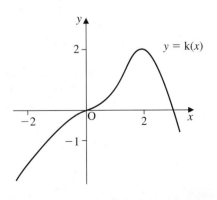

20   Graphs of functions

U   7   Part of the graph of $y = f(x)$ is shown.
    (a) Copy the graph and on the
    same diagram sketch the graph
    of $y = f(-x)$.
    (b) Annotate your sketch with the
    images of the points
    A, B, C and D, and give their
    coordinates.

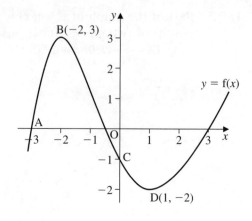

U   8   Part of the graph of $y = g(x)$ is shown.
Copy the graph and on the same
diagram sketch the graph of $y = g(-x)$.

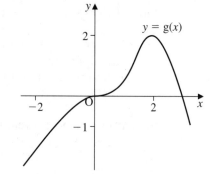

U   9   Part of the graph of $y = f(x)$
is shown.
Copy the graph and on the
same diagram sketch the
graph of $y = 2f(x)$. Annotate
your sketch with the images of
the points A and B, and give
their coordinates.

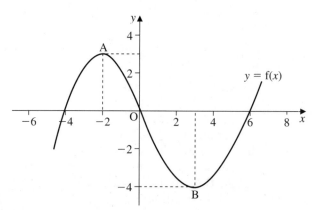

U   10   Part of the graph of $y = f(x)$ is shown.
Copy the graph and on the same diagram sketch the graph
of $y = \frac{1}{3}f(x)$.

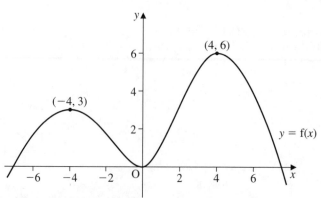

U 11 Part of the graph of $y = f(x)$ is shown.
Copy the graph and on the same diagram
sketch the graph of $y = f(3x)$.

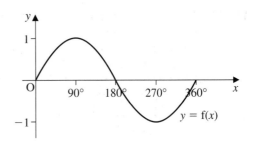

C 12 The diagram shows the graph of $y = f(x)$.

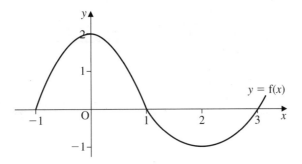

Sketch the graph of $y = -f(x - 1)$.

C 13 The diagram shows a sketch of the graphs of the quadratic
functions $y = f(x)$ and $y = -f(x + 2)$.
  (a) $f(x)$ has a turning point at $(0, 2)$ and passes through
       $(-1, 3)$. Find $f(x)$.
  (b) Find the coordinates of the maximum turning point of
       $y = -f(x + 2)$.

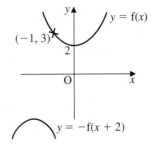

C 14 The diagram shows a sketch of the parabola $y = f(x)$.
  (a) Copy the sketch of $y = f(x)$ and on it draw the
       parabola $y = -f(x) + 5$.
  (b) If $g(x) = 5 - f(x)$ state the
       coordinates of (i) the turning point
       and (ii) the points of intersection with
       the axes for $y = g(x)$.
  (c) Find a formula for $g(x)$ in terms of x.

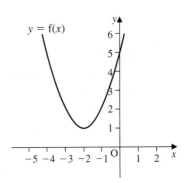

C 15 The diagram shows part of the graph of a
function of the form $y = \log_a (x - b)$.
Find the values of a and b.

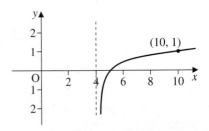

C 16   A sketch of the graph of the cubic function f is shown.
It passes through the origin, has a maximum turning point at $(a, 1)$ and a minimum turning point at $(b, 0)$.
Make a copy of this diagram and on it sketch the graph of $y = 2 - f(x)$, indicating the coordinates of the turning points.   [Higher]

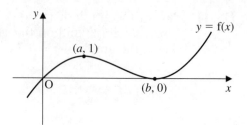

Test yourself	**What to review**

If your answer is incorrect:

U 1   The diagram shows part of the graph of $y = f(x)$.

Heinemann Higher Mathematics Chapter 3, pages 35 to 36 and 39 and 40

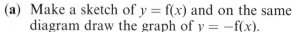

(a) Make a sketch of $y = f(x)$ and on the same diagram draw the graph of $y = -f(x)$.

(b) Make a second sketch of $y = f(x)$ and on the same diagram draw the graph of $y = f(x) - 1$.

U 2   The diagram shows part of the graph of $y = f(x)$ and, shown by a dotted line, the graph of a related function.

Heinemann Higher Mathematics Chapter 3, pages 41 to 42

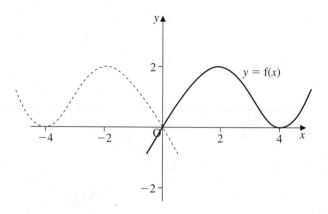

Write down the equation of the related function.

C 3   The diagram shows part of the graph of $y = g(x)$ and,
shown by a dotted line, the graph of a related function.

*Heinemann Higher
Mathematics Chapter 3,
pages 35, 36, 39 and 40*

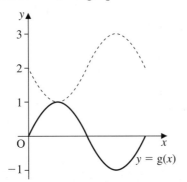

Write down the equation of the related function.

C 4   Part of the graph of $y = f(x)$ is shown in the diagram.
On separate diagrams, sketch the graphs of:
(a) $y = f(x + 1)$ **(b)** $y = -2f(x)$.

*Heinemann Higher
Mathematics Chapter 3,
pages 37, 38, 42 and 43*

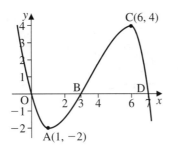

Indicate on each graph the images of O, A, B, C
and D.   [Higher]

Test yourself answers

1 (a)

(b)

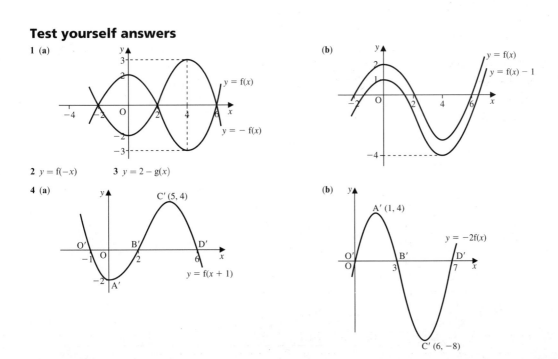

2 $y = f(-x)$ **3** $y = 2 - g(x)$

4 (a)

(b)

4 Trigonometry: graphs and equations

Key points to remember

1 A graph which consists of a repeated pattern is described as **periodic**.

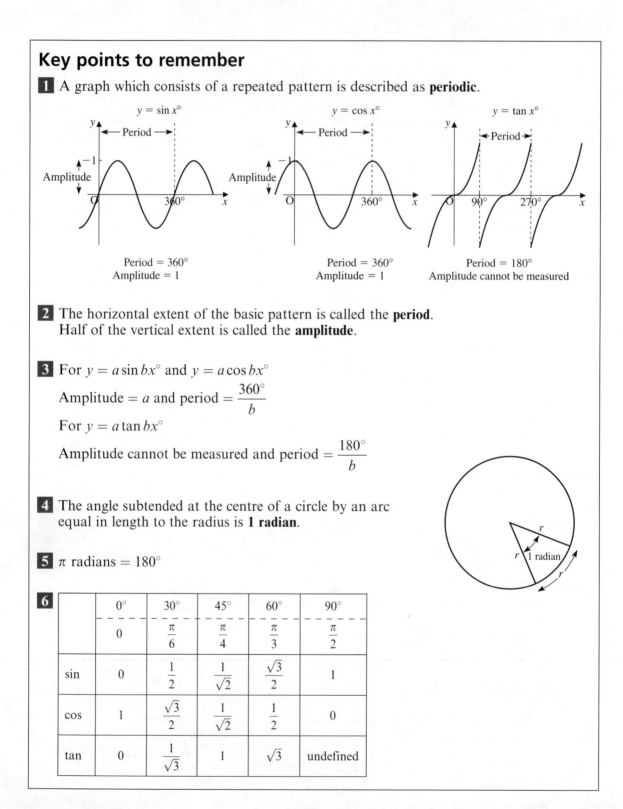

$y = \sin x°$

Period = 360°
Amplitude = 1

$y = \cos x°$

Period = 360°
Amplitude = 1

$y = \tan x°$

Period = 180°
Amplitude cannot be measured

2 The horizontal extent of the basic pattern is called the **period**.
Half of the vertical extent is called the **amplitude**.

3 For $y = a \sin bx°$ and $y = a \cos bx°$

Amplitude $= a$ and period $= \dfrac{360°}{b}$

For $y = a \tan bx°$

Amplitude cannot be measured and period $= \dfrac{180°}{b}$

4 The angle subtended at the centre of a circle by an arc equal in length to the radius is **1 radian**.

5 π radians $= 180°$

6

	0°	30°	45°	60°	90°
	0	$\dfrac{\pi}{6}$	$\dfrac{\pi}{4}$	$\dfrac{\pi}{3}$	$\dfrac{\pi}{2}$
sin	0	$\dfrac{1}{2}$	$\dfrac{1}{\sqrt{2}}$	$\dfrac{\sqrt{3}}{2}$	1
cos	1	$\dfrac{\sqrt{3}}{2}$	$\dfrac{1}{\sqrt{2}}$	$\dfrac{1}{2}$	0
tan	0	$\dfrac{1}{\sqrt{3}}$	1	$\sqrt{3}$	undefined

Outcome 2

Associate functions and graphs.
See Chapters 2 and 3 for other functions and graphs.

Performance criteria

PC(a)   Sketch and identify related graphs and functions.

U   Example 1

Sketch the graph of the function $y = 3\sin 2x° + 1$.

Solution

Start with the graph of $y = \sin x°$.

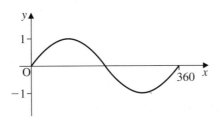

| Squeeze horizontally by a factor of $\frac{1}{2}$ | Stretch vertically by a factor of 3 | Slide vertically 1 unit upwards |

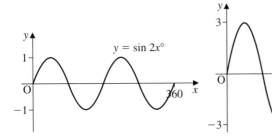 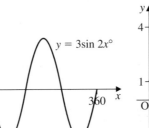 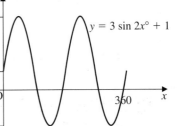

U   Example 2

The diagram shows part of the graph
$y = a\cos 2x°$.
(a) State the value of a.
(b) Write the equation of the related graph.

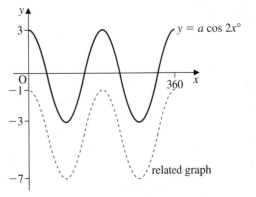

Solution

(a) The amplitude is 3, so $a = 3$.
(b) Since the related graph is 4 units below
    $y = 3\cos 2x°$, its equation is
    $y = 3\cos 2x° - 4$.

C Example 3

The diagram shows part of the graph
of $y = a \cos(x - b)° + c$.
Find the values of a, b and c.

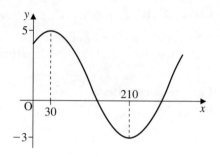

Solution

$$\text{Period} = 360°$$

$$\text{Amplitude} = \frac{5 - (-3)}{2} = 4$$

$$\text{Horizontal shift} = 30 \text{ to the right}$$
$$\text{Vertical shift} = 1 \text{ up}$$

The graph has equation $y = 4 \cos(x - 30)° + 1$.

C Example 4

Find the coordinates of the maximum turning point
of the graph of $y = 3 \sin\left(x + \dfrac{\pi}{3}\right)$ for $0 \leqslant x \leqslant 2\pi$.

Solution

Since $-1 \leqslant \sin x \leqslant 1$ then $-3 \leqslant 3 \sin\left(x + \dfrac{\pi}{3}\right) \leqslant 3$

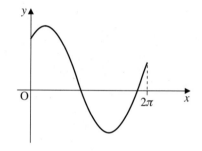

The maximum value of the function is 3, when

$$3 \sin\left(x + \frac{\pi}{3}\right) = 3$$

$$\sin\left(x + \frac{\pi}{3}\right) = 1$$

$$x + \frac{\pi}{3} = \frac{\pi}{2}$$

$$x = \frac{\pi}{6}$$

The maximum turning point is at $\left(\dfrac{\pi}{6}, 3\right)$.

C Example 5

Solve $4 \cos^2 x - 1 = 0$ for $0 \leqslant x \leqslant 2\pi$.

Solution

$4 \cos^2 x - 1 = 0$

$4 \cos^2 x = 1$

$\cos^2 x = \frac{1}{4}$

$\cos x = \pm \frac{1}{2}$

When $\cos x = \frac{1}{2}$, $x = \dfrac{\pi}{3}$ or $\dfrac{5\pi}{3}$

When $\cos x = -\frac{1}{2}$, $x = \dfrac{2\pi}{3}$ or $\dfrac{4\pi}{3}$

$x = \dfrac{\pi}{3}$ or $\dfrac{2\pi}{3}$ or $\dfrac{4\pi}{3}$ or $\dfrac{5\pi}{3}$.

C Example 6

The graph shows the depth, d metres, of water in a harbour t hours after midnight. The depth of water can be modelled by the function $d(t) = 2\cos 30t° + 2$. A boat anchored in the harbour has a draught of 3 metres. Between which hours will it be grounded?

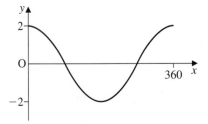

Solution
The boat will float if $d(t) > 3$

so $2\cos 30t° + 2 > 3$

$\cos 30t° > \frac{1}{2}$

When $\cos 30t° = \frac{1}{2}$ then $30t = 60$ or 300

$t = 2$ or 10

The boat will be grounded between 0200 hours and 1000 hours.

Revision exercise 4

U   **1** The diagrams show part of the graph of $y = \sin x°$ and the graph of a related function. State the equation of the related function.

(a)   **(b)**

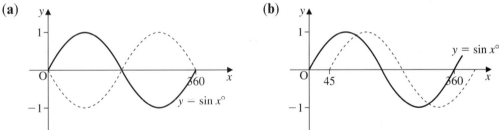

U   **2** The diagrams show part of the graph of $y = \cos x°$ and the graph of a related function. State the equation of the related function.

(a)   **(b)**

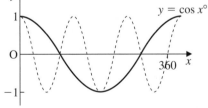
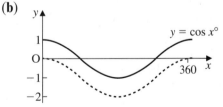

U   **3** The diagram shows a graph of the form $f(x) = 2\cos x°$. Sketch the graph of
(a) $y = f(x) + 4$
(b) $y = f(2x)$
(c) $y = 2f(x + 60) - 1$

U 4 Write down the trigonometric function represented by each graph.

(a)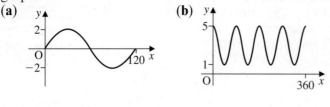

(b)

(c)

U 5 Sketch and annotate the graph of each of the following functions for $0 \leqslant x \leqslant 360$.

(a) $y = 3 \sin x° + 1$ (b) $y = 4 \cos 2x° - 5$

(c) $y = 2 \sin (x - 45)° - 3$ (d) $y = 1 - \sin 3x°$

U 6 The graph of the function $y = 3 \cos \left(x - \dfrac{\pi}{4} \right)$ is shown. Find the values of a, b, c and d.

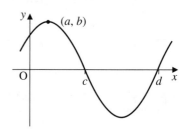

U 7 Sketch the graph of $y = 2 \sin (x - 30)°$ for $0 \leqslant x \leqslant 360$.

[Higher]

C 8 Find the maximum value of each of the following functions.

(a) $y = 4 \cos x° + 1$ (b) $y = 7 \sin (3x - 120)° - 2$ (c) $y = (1 - \cos x)^2 + 3$

C 9 Find the values of θ, where $0 \leqslant \theta \leqslant 2\pi$, for which

$4 \cos \left(2\theta - \dfrac{\pi}{4} \right)$ has its maximum value.   [Higher]

C 10 Find the values of θ ($0 \leqslant \theta \leqslant \pi$) for which

$V = 2 \sin \left(3\theta - \dfrac{\pi}{4} \right)$ has its maximum value.   [Higher]

C 11 Solve each of the following equations for $0 \leqslant x \leqslant \pi$.

(a) $2 \cos^2 x - 1 = 0$ (b) $3 \tan^2 x = 1$ (c) $2 \sin^2 x + \sin x - 1 = 0$

C 12 Solve $2 \sin 3x° - 1 = 0$ for $0 \leqslant x \leqslant 180$.   [Higher]

C 13 Solve the equation $2 \cos^2 x = \frac{1}{2}$ for $0 \leqslant x \leqslant \pi$.   [Higher]

C 14 If $f(a) = 6 \sin^2 a - \cos a$, express $f(a)$ in the form $p \cos^2 a + q \cos a + r$. Hence solve, correct to 3 decimal places, the equation $6 \sin^2 a - \cos a = 5$.   [Higher]

C 15 The minimum depth, d metres, of water in a harbour t hours after midnight is given by $d(t) = 5 + 2 \sin 30t°$ where $0 \leqslant t \leqslant 24$.

(a) A ship with a draught of 4 metres is in harbour at midnight. By what time must it leave to prevent grounding?

(b) What is the next time it can return to harbour?

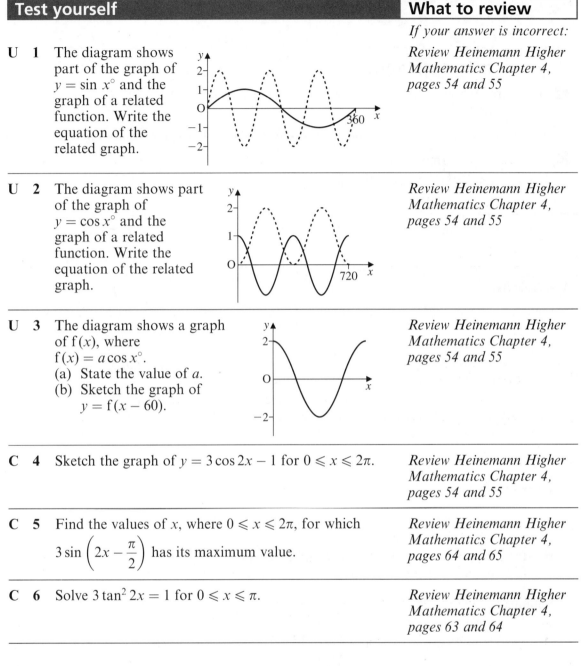

Test yourself | **What to review**

If your answer is incorrect:

U 1 The diagram shows part of the graph of $y = \sin x°$ and the graph of a related function. Write the equation of the related graph.

Review Heinemann Higher Mathematics Chapter 4, pages 54 and 55

U 2 The diagram shows part of the graph of $y = \cos x°$ and the graph of a related function. Write the equation of the related graph.

Review Heinemann Higher Mathematics Chapter 4, pages 54 and 55

U 3 The diagram shows a graph of $f(x)$, where $f(x) = a\cos x°$.
(a) State the value of a.
(b) Sketch the graph of $y = f(x - 60)$.

Review Heinemann Higher Mathematics Chapter 4, pages 54 and 55

C 4 Sketch the graph of $y = 3\cos 2x - 1$ for $0 \leqslant x \leqslant 2\pi$.

Review Heinemann Higher Mathematics Chapter 4, pages 54 and 55

C 5 Find the values of x, where $0 \leqslant x \leqslant 2\pi$, for which $3\sin\left(2x - \dfrac{\pi}{2}\right)$ has its maximum value.

Review Heinemann Higher Mathematics Chapter 4, pages 64 and 65

C 6 Solve $3\tan^2 2x = 1$ for $0 \leqslant x \leqslant \pi$.

Review Heinemann Higher Mathematics Chapter 4, pages 63 and 64

Test yourself answers

1 $y = 2\sin 3x°$ **2** $y = 1 - \cos x°$ **3 (a)** 2 **(b)**   **4**

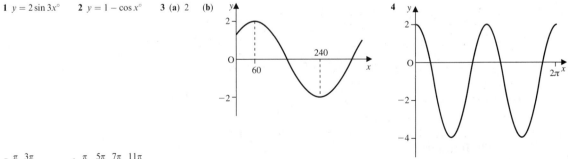

5 $\dfrac{\pi}{2}, \dfrac{3\pi}{2}$ **6** $\dfrac{\pi}{12}, \dfrac{5\pi}{12}, \dfrac{7\pi}{12}, \dfrac{11\pi}{12}$

5 Recurrence relations

Key points to remember

1 A recurrence relation describes a sequence in which each term is a function of previous terms.

2 A sequence defined by $u_{n+1} = au_n + b$, $a \neq 0$ is called a **linear recurrence relation**.

3 For a linear recurrence relation $u_{n+1} = au_n + b$:
If $-1 < a < 1$, then u_n tends to a limit
If u_n tends to a limit, L, then $L = \dfrac{b}{1 - a}$

Outcome 4

Design and interpret mathematical models of situations involving recurrence relations.

Performance criteria

PC(a) Define and interpret a recurrence relation in the form $u_{n+1} = mu_n + c$ (m, c constants) in a mathematical model.

PC(b) Find and interpret the limit of a sequence generated by a recurrence relation in a mathematical model (where the limit exists).

U Example 1

A sequence is defined by the recurrence relation
$u_{n+1} = 0.5u_n + 12$, $u_0 = 10$.
(a) Find the next four terms of this recurrence relation.
(b) Find the limit of this recurrence relation if it exists.

Solution

(a) $\begin{aligned} u_1 &= 0.5u_0 + 12 \\ &= 0.5 \times 10 + 12 \\ &= 17 \end{aligned}$ $\begin{aligned} u_2 &= 0.5u_1 + 12 \\ &= 0.5 \times 17 + 12 \\ &= 20.5 \end{aligned}$

$\begin{aligned} u_3 &= 0.5u_2 + 12 \\ &= 0.5 \times 20.5 + 12 \\ &= 22.25 \end{aligned}$ $\begin{aligned} u_4 &= 0.5u_3 + 12 \\ &= 0.5 \times 22.25 + 12 \\ &= 23.125 \end{aligned}$

(b) $a = 0.5$, so $-1 < a < 1$ and therefore a limit exists.

$$L = \frac{b}{1 - a} \qquad \text{or} \qquad \begin{aligned} L &= 0.5L + 12 \\ L - 0.5L &= 12 \\ 0.5L &= 12 \\ L &= 24 \end{aligned}$$

$$= \frac{12}{1 - 0.5}$$

$$= 24$$

U Example 2

In an old car it is estimated that oil leaks from the engine at a rate of 20% per week. The engine contains 5 litres of oil immediately after being filled. The engine will be irreparably damaged if the volume of oil drops below 3.5 litres. If the engine is topped up with 0.5 litres of oil each week:

(a) write down a recurrence relation that describes the situation above

(b) find the limit and explain what it means in the context of the question.

Solution

(a) Let u_n = the volume of oil in the engine after n weeks.
$u_{n+1} = 0.8u_n + 0.5$, $u_0 = 5$

(b) $a = 0.8$, so $-1 < a < 1$ and therefore a limit exists.

$$L = \frac{b}{1-a}$$
$$= \frac{0.5}{1-0.8}$$
$$= 2.5$$

or

$$L = 0.8L + 0.5$$
$$L - 0.8L = 0.5$$
$$0.2L = 0.5$$
$$L = 2.5$$

Since $2.5 < 3.5$, irrepairable damage will be done to the engine if this situation continues.

C Example 3

The sum of £2000 is placed in an investment account on January 1st and thereafter £50 is placed in the account on the first day of each month.

● Interest at the rate of 0.25% per month is credited to the account on the last day of each month.

● This interest is calculated on the amount in the account on the first day of the month.

(a) How much is in the account on June 30th?

(b) On what date does the account first exceed £2500?

(c) Find a recurrence relation that describes the amount in the account, explaining your notation carefully.

Solution

(a)   Feb 1 balance $= 1.0025 \times 2000 + 50 \quad = 2055$

 Mar 1 balance $= 1.0025 \times 2055 + 50 \quad = 2110.14$

 Apr 1 balance $= 1.0025 \times 2110.14 + 50 \ = 2165.41$

 May 1 balance $= 1.0025 \times 2165.41 + 50 \ = 2220.83$

 Jun 1 balance $= 1.0025 \times 2220.83 + 50 \ = 2276.38$

 Jun 30 balance $= 1.0025 \times 2276.38 \quad\quad = 2282.07$

 The balance on 30th June is £2282.07

(b)   Aug 1 balance $= 1.0025 \times 2332.07 + 50\ = 2387.90$

Sep 1 balance $= 1.0025 \times 2387.90 + 50\ = 2443.87$

Oct 1 balance $= 1.0025 \times 2443.87 + 50\ = 2499.98$

Nov 1 balance $= 1.0025 \times 2499.98 + 50\ = 2556.23$

Oct 30 balance $= 2556.23 - 50 \qquad\quad = 2506.23$

The account first exceeds £2500 on 30th October.

(c) $u_{n+1} = 1.0025u_n + 50$, $u_0 = 2000$ where u_n is the amount in the account on the first day of the nth month after the initial deposit.

Revision exercise 5

U **1** Find the next four terms and the limit, if it exists, for each recurrence relation.
(a) $u_{n+1} = 0.1u_n + 4.5$, $u_0 = 4$
(b) $u_{n+1} = 0.5u_n - 8$, $u_0 = 20$
(c) $u_{n+1} = 1.5u_n + 100$, $u_0 = 2$
(b) $u_{n+1} = -0.2u_n + 10$, $u_0 = 8$

U **2** It is estimated that the area of a pond affected by algae increases by 5 square metres each week. A gardener clears 25% of the affected area each week. If the original area affected by the algae was 30 square metres:
(a) write down a recurrence relation that describes the situation above
(b) find the limit and explain what it means in the context of the question.

U **3** An organic gardener discovers that 200 aphids are born each week in his greenhouse during the summer. He introduces a parasite which kills 50% of the aphids each week. If there were 600 aphids at the beginning of the summer:
(a) write down a recurrence relation that describes this situation
(b) find the limit and explain what it means in the context of question.

U **4** Kathryn was given £25 on her 13th birthday and £20 on each birthday thereafter. She invested these gifts in a building society that pays interest at a rate of 3% per annum.
(a) Write down a recurrence relation that describes this situation.
(b) Calculate the expected balance in the account on her 18th birthday.

C **5** A sequence is defined by the recurrence relation $u_{n+1} = 0.65u_n + 7$, $u_0 = 10$.
(a) Calculate the value of u_2.
(b) What is the smallest value of n for which $u_n > 18$?
(c) Find the limit of this sequence as $n \to \infty$.

C **6** A sequence is defined by the recurrence relation $u_{n+1} = 0.3u_n + 5$ with the first term u_1.
(a) Explain why this sequence has a limit as n tends to infinity.
(b) Find the **exact** value of this limit.   [Higher]

C 7 A market gardener has a 60 square metre greenhouse. Each square metre contains 25 mature basil plants. To maintain stocks, she requires to have 500 mature plants at any one time. She estimates that 40% of mature plants are picked each week, while 150 plants mature over the same period of time. Will stocks be maintained at an acceptable level?

C 8 A chemical plant has requested permission to disperse 45 units of chemical waste per week into the sea. It is estimated that the natural action of the sea will remove 25% of waste per week. What is the long-term effect of these conditions?

C 9 On January 1st Colin deposits a sum of £500 in an investment account and thereafter £200 is placed in the account on the first day of each month.
  ● Interest at the rate of 0.5% per month is credited to the account on the last day of each month.
  ● This interest is calculated on the amount in the account on the first day of the month.
  (a) How much is in the account on June 30th?
  (b) On what date does the account first exceed £2000?
  (c) Find a recurrence relation that describes the amount in the account, explaining your notation carefully.

C 10 Trees are sprayed weekly with the pesticide "Killpest", whose manufacturers claim it will destroy 65% of all pests. Between the weekly sprayings, it is estimated that 500 new pests invade the trees. A new pesticide, "Pestkill", comes onto the market. The manufacturers claim it will destroy 85% of existing pests but it is estimated that 650 new pests per week will invade the trees.
Which pesticide will be more effective?   [Higher]

C 11 A local authority has to put the cleaning of its parks out to tender. Firm A claims that it will remove 95% of all litter dropped each week. It is known that the public drops 25 kg of litter each week.
Firm B claims that it will remove 85% of all litter dropped each week. They also claim that they will have litter bins strategically placed and that this will lead to the public dropping only 20 kg per week.
If the two firms charge the same, which firm should the council employ?

C 12 The numbers 20, 18 and 17 are three consecutive terms of the linear recurrence relation $u_n = au_{n-1} + b$. Find the values of a and b.

C 13 The amounts in a bank account at the end of three consecutive years were £1500, £1675 and £1858.75 respectively. The interest rate remained constant over this period, while an extra fixed amount was also invested each year.
What was the interest rate and the amount invested each year?

34 Recurrence relations

<table>
<tr>
<td colspan="2" style="background:black;color:white">Test yourself</td>
<td style="background:black;color:white">What to review</td>
</tr>
<tr>
<td></td>
<td></td>
<td>If your answer is incorrect:</td>
</tr>
<tr>
<td>U</td>
<td>1 Find the next four terms and the exact value of the limit, if it exists, for this recurrence relation:

$u_{n+1} = 0.25u_n + 3.5, u_0 = 4$</td>
<td>Review Heinemann Higher Mathematics Chapter 5, pages 73 and 77</td>
</tr>
<tr>
<td>U</td>
<td>2 A doctor administers 20 ml of a drug to a patient each day. Over the same period it is estimated that 75% of the drug in the patient's bloodstream is removed. If the level in the bloodstream rises above 30 ml, the drug becomes toxic.
(a) Write down a recurrence relation that describes this situation.
(b) Find the limit and explain what it means in the context of the question.</td>
<td>Review Heinemann Higher Mathematics Chapter 5, page 77</td>
</tr>
<tr>
<td>C</td>
<td>3 A sequence is defined by the recurrence relation:

$u_{n+1} = 0.45u_n + 11, u_0 = 15$

(a) Calculate the value of u_2.
(b) What is the smallest value of n for which $u_n > 19$?
(c) Find the limit of this sequence as $n \to \infty$.</td>
<td>Review Heinemann Higher Mathematics Chapter 5, page 77</td>
</tr>
<tr>
<td>C</td>
<td>4 A farmer sprays a test plot monthly with Weedal. He finds that it destroys 80% of weeds while 20 new weeds grow by the end of each month. In another test plot he weeds by hand and finds that he can remove 90% of the weeds while 25 new weeds grow each month.
Which method of weed control is more effective?</td>
<td>Review Heinemann Higher Mathematics Chapter 5, page 77</td>
</tr>
<tr>
<td>C</td>
<td>5 The numbers 100, 275 and 493.75 are three consecutive terms of the linear recurrence relation $u_n = au_{n-1} + b$. Find the values of a and b.</td>
<td>Review Heinemann Higher Mathematics Chapter 5, page 79</td>
</tr>
</table>

Test yourself answers

1 4.5, 4.625, 4.65625, 4.6640625, $L = \dfrac{14}{3}$ **2 (a)** $u_{n+1} = 0.25u_n + 20, u_0 = 0$ **(b)** $L = 26\dfrac{2}{3}$ therefore the drug is non-toxic since $26\dfrac{2}{3} < 30$

3 (a) 18.9875   **(b)** $n = 3$ **(c)** 20

4 Weedal: $L = 25$; hand method: $L = 27\dfrac{7}{9}$. Hence Weedal controls weeds better in the long term.

5 $a = 1.25, b = 150$.

6 Differentiation

Key points to remember

1 The rate of change of a function f(x) can be written as f'(x) and is called the **derived function**.

2 The derivative of a function represents:
- the rate of change of a function
- the gradient of the tangent to the function.

3 $f'(x) = \lim\limits_{h \to 0} \dfrac{f(x + h) - f(x)}{h}$

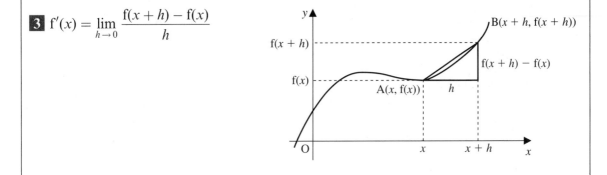

4 If f(x) = ax^n then f'(x) = anx^{n-1}, where a is a constant and n is a rational number.

5 If f(x) = g(x) + h(x) then f'(x) = g'(x) + h'(x)

6 $\dfrac{dy}{dx} = f'(x)$

7 Since a tangent is a straight line, its equation may be given by $y - b = m(x - a)$. Hence, to find the equation of the tangent at any point on a curve we need to determine:
- the coordinates (a, b) of the point

- the gradient, m, at that point by finding $\dfrac{dy}{dx}$

8 For any curve:
If f'(x) > 0 in a given interval then f(x) is strictly increasing in that interval.
If f'(x) < 0 in a given interval then f(x) is strictly decreasing in that interval.

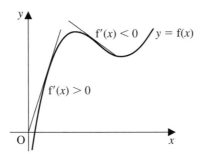

9 Stationary points occur when $f'(x) = 0$.
The nature of a stationary point depends on the gradient on either side of it.
Stationary points may be one of the following types:

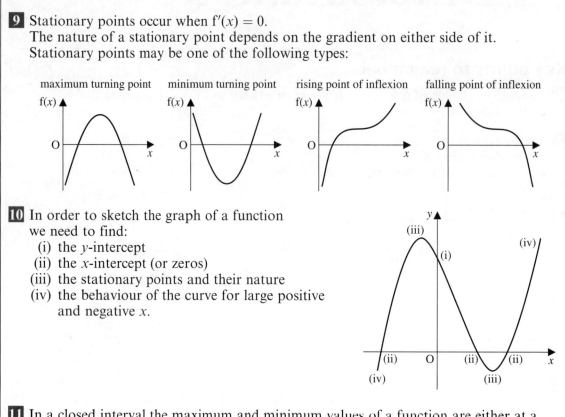

| maximum turning point | minimum turning point | rising point of inflexion | falling point of inflexion |

10 In order to sketch the graph of a function
we need to find:
  (i) the y-intercept
  (ii) the x-intercept (or zeros)
  (iii) the stationary points and their nature
  (iv) the behaviour of the curve for large positive
      and negative x.

11 In a closed interval the maximum and minimum values of a function are either at a
stationary point or at an end point of the interval.

Outcome 3

Use basic differentiation.

Performance criteria

PC(a)   Differentiate functions reducible to the sums of powers of x.

PC(b)   Determine the gradient of a tangent to a curve by differentiation.

PC(c)   Determine the coordinates of the stationary points on a curve and justify their
        nature using differentiation.

U   Example 1
Find $f'(x)$ when $f(x) = 4x^3 + \sqrt{x} + 2$.

Solution
$$f(x) = 4x^3 + \sqrt{x} + 2$$
$$= 4x^3 + x^{\frac{1}{2}} + 2$$
$$f'(x) = 12x^2 + \tfrac{1}{2}x^{-\frac{1}{2}}$$
$$= 12x^2 + \frac{1}{2\sqrt{x}}$$

U Example 2

Given that $y = \dfrac{x^5 + 2}{x^2}$, find $\dfrac{dy}{dx}$.

Solution

$$y = \frac{x^5 + 2}{x^2}$$

$$= \frac{x^5}{x^2} + \frac{2}{x^2}$$

$$= x^3 + 2x^{-2}$$

$$\frac{dy}{dx} = 3x^2 + (-4)x^{-3}$$

$$= 3x^2 - \frac{4}{x^3}$$

U Example 3

The diagram shows the graph of $y = (2 - x)(x + 3)$.
(a) Find the gradient of the tangent at $(-1, 6)$.
(b) Hence find its equation.

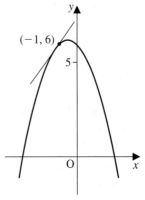

Solution

(a) $y = (2 - x)(x + 3) = 6 - x - x^2$

$$\frac{dy}{dx} = -1 - 2x$$

When $x = -1$ $\dfrac{dy}{dx} = -1 - 2 \times (-1)$

$$= 1$$

Hence gradient of tangent $= 1$

(b) $y - b = m(x - a)$

$$y - 6 = 1(x - (-1))$$

$$y = x + 7$$

U Example 4

Find the rate of change of $f(x) = \dfrac{x^4 - 1}{x}$ at $x = 2$.

Solution

$$f(x) = \frac{x^4 - 1}{x} = \frac{x^4}{x} - \frac{1}{x} = x^3 - x^{-1}$$

$$f'(x) = 3x^2 - (-1)x^{-2}$$

$$= 3x^2 + \frac{1}{x^2}$$

$$f'(2) = 3 \times 2^2 + \frac{1}{2^2}$$

$$= 12\tfrac{1}{4}$$

U Example 5

For the curve with equation $y = 2x^3 - 9x^2 - 24x + 6$ find the coordinates of the stationary points and determine their nature.

Solution

$y = 2x^3 - 9x^2 - 24x + 6$

$$\frac{dy}{dx} = 6x^2 - 18x - 24$$

Stationary points occur when $\frac{dy}{dx} = 0$

$$6x^2 - 18x - 24 = 0$$
$$6(x + 1)(x - 4) = 0$$
$$x + 1 = 0 \quad x - 4 = 0$$
$$x = -1 \quad x = 4$$

When $x = -1$, $y = 19$ and when $x = 4$, $y = -106$.
The stationary points are $(-1, 19)$ and $(4, -106)$.

Consider the gradient, $\frac{dy}{dx}$, in the neighbourhood of each stationary point.

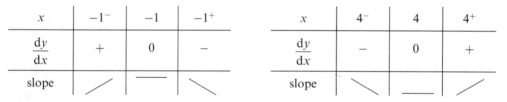

x	-1^-	-1	-1^+
$\frac{dy}{dx}$	$+$	0	$-$
slope	/	—	\

x	4^-	4	4^+
$\frac{dy}{dx}$	$-$	0	$+$
slope	\	—	/

There is a maximum turning point at $(-1, 19)$ and a minimum turning point at $(4, -106)$.

C Example 6

The graph shows $y = f(x)$ for $-2 \leqslant x \leqslant 4$ where $f(x)$ is a cubic function. Sketch the graph of $y = f'(x)$ for the same domain.

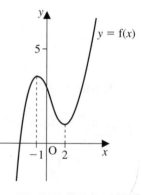

Solution

From the graph of $y = f(x)$ we can determine the following:

	$x < -1$	$x = -1$	$-1 < x < 2$	$x = 2$	$x > 2$
$f'(x)$	+ve	zero	−ve	zero	+ve

Hence the graph of $y = f'(x)$ is as shown opposite.

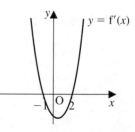

C Example 7

Sarah's drinking beaker is in the shape of a cylinder with a hemispherical lid and a circular flat base. The radius of the cylinder is r cm and the height is h cm. The volume of the cylinder is 400 cm^3.

(a) Show that the surface area of plastic, $A(r)$, needed to make the beaker is given by $A(r) = 3\pi r^2 + \dfrac{800}{r}$.

Note: The curved surface area of a hemisphere of radius r is $2\pi r^2$.

(b) Find the value of r which ensures that the surface area of plastic is minimised.   [Higher]

Sarah's Can

Solution

(a) Area of base $= \pi r^2$
     Area of hemisphere $= 2\pi r^2$ To find h:
     Area of side $= 2\pi rh$ Volume of cylinder $= \pi r^2 h = 400$

$$h = \frac{400}{\pi r^2}$$

Total area $= \pi r^2 + 2\pi r^2 + 2\pi rh$

$$A(r) = \pi r^2 + 2\pi r^2 + 2\pi r \times \frac{400}{\pi r^2}$$

$$= 3\pi r^2 + \frac{800}{r}$$

(b) For a minimum to occur, $A'(r) = 0$

$$A(r) = 3\pi r^2 + \frac{800}{r}$$

$$= 3\pi r^2 + 800\, r^{-1}$$

$$A'(r) = 6\pi r - 800\, r^{-2}$$

$$= 6\pi r - \frac{800}{r^2}$$

$$6\pi r - \frac{800}{r^2} = 0$$

$$6\pi r^3 - 800 = 0$$

$$r^3 = \frac{800}{6\pi}$$

$$r = 3.5 \text{ (to 1 decimal place)}$$

r	3.5^-	3.5	3.5^+
$A'(r)$	$-$	0	$+$
slope	$\searrow$	$-$	$\nearrow$

Hence a minimum occurs when $r = 3.5$ cm.

Revision exercise 6

U 1 Find $f'(x)$ for each of the following.

  (a) $f(x) = x(x^2 + 2x)$ (b) $f(x) = \dfrac{x^5 - 1}{x^2}$

  (c) $f(x) = \dfrac{x^2 - 3}{x^4}$

U 2 Find the rate of change of each of the following functions at the given value of x.

  (a) $f(x) = 2x^3 + x^2 - \dfrac{3}{2}x + 4$ when $x = 2$

  (b) $f(x) = \dfrac{1}{x} + \dfrac{1}{x^2} - \dfrac{1}{2x^3}$ when $x = 1$

U 3 Find $\dfrac{dy}{dx}$ for each of the following.

  (a) $y = \sqrt{x}(x^2 - x)$ (b) $y = (\sqrt{x} - 2)(4 - \sqrt{x})$

  (c) $y = \dfrac{x^3 - x^2 - x + 1}{x^2}$

U 4 Find the gradients of the tangents drawn in each of the following diagrams.

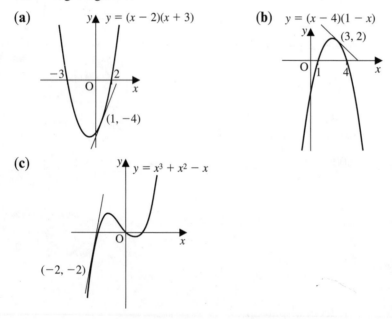

U 5 A curve has the equation $y = -x^4 + 4x^3 - 2$.
An incomplete sketch is shown in the diagram.
  (a) Find the coordinates of the stationary points.
  (b) Determine the nature of the stationary points.   [Higher]

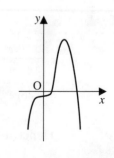

U 6 Find the stationary points of the curves with the following equations and determine their nature, justifying your answer.

(a) $y = 8x^3 + 3x^2 - 9x - 3$ (b) $y = 12x^3 - 3x^2 - 6x + 2$

(c) $y = 4x^3 - 18x^2 + 24x - 3$

(d) $y = 8x^3 - 4x^2 + 6$

C 7 Find the equation of the tangent to each curve.

(a) $y = x^3 - 2x^2 + 4$ at (2, 4)

(b) $y = \dfrac{-1}{x}$ at (−1, 1)

C 8 Find the equation of the tangent to $y = x^2 + 3x + 2$ parallel to the line $y = 2x + 1$.

C 9 (a) For the curve $y = x^3 + 3x^2 - 7x + 2$ find the points of contact of the tangents with gradient 2.

(b) Find the equations of each of these tangents.

C 10 At what point is the tangent to the curve $y = x^2 + 5$

(a) parallel to the line $12x = y + 17$

(b) perpendicular to the line $3y = 2 - x$?

C 11 Sketch the graph of f'(x) for each of the following curves.

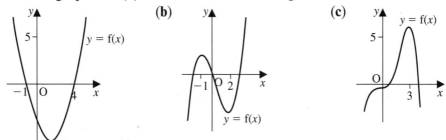

(a) $y = f(x)$ (b) $y = f(x)$ (c) $y = f(x)$

C 12 An open tank is to be designed in the shape of a cuboid with a square base, the total surface area of the base and the four walls together being $100\,\text{m}^2$.

(a) If the length of the base is $x\,\text{cm}$, show that the volume, $V(x)$, is given by $V(x) = \dfrac{x}{4}(100 - x^2)$.

(b) Find the length of the base that makes the volume of the tank a maximum.

C 13 The distance from a fixed point of a particle moving in a straight line is given by $d(t) = 12t - 15t^2 + 4t^3$ where t is the time in seconds. Find the speed of the particle (rate of change) after 2 seconds.

42 Differentiation

| Test yourself | What to review |

U 1 Given that $y = \dfrac{5 - x^4}{x^2}$ find $\dfrac{dy}{dx}$.

If your answer is incorrect:
Review Heinemann Higher Mathematics Chapter 6, pages 94 to 96

U 2 Find the gradient of the tangent to the curve $y = (x + 5)(x - 2)$ shown in the diagram.

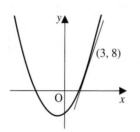

Review Heinemann Higher Mathematics Chapter 6, pages 98 and 99

U 3 Find the coordinates of the stationary points of the curve with equation $y = 2x^3 - 3x^2 - 12x + 5$ and determine their nature.

Review Heinemann Higher Mathematics Chapter 6, pages 104 to 106

U 4 Find the rate of change of $y = \dfrac{\sqrt{x} + 5}{x^2}$ when $x = 4$.

Review Heinemann Higher Mathematics Chapter 6, pages 92 to 96

C 5 Find the equation of the tangent to the curve $y = x^3 - 9x^2 + 20x - 8$ at the point $(1, 4)$.

Review Heinemann Higher Mathematics Chapter 6, page 100

C 6 Find the equation of the tangents to the curve $y = x^3 - 6x^2 + 12x + 2$ that are parallel to the line $y = 3x$.

Review Heinemann Higher Mathematics Chapter 6, page 100

C 7 The diagram shows the graph of the cubic function $y = f(x)$.

Review Heinemann Higher Mathematics Chapter 6, pages 109 and 110

Sketch the graph of $y = f'(x)$.

C **8** A gardener requires a rectangular plot of $12\,\text{m}^2$ to plant some vegetables. He is planning to place edging around the perimeter of the plot. If one side of the plot is x metres:

Review Heinemann Higher Mathematics Chapter 6, pages 111 to 114

(**a**) show that the perimeter in metres, $P(x)$, can be expressed as $P(x) = 2x + \dfrac{24}{x}$

(**b**) find the dimensions of the rectangle with the minimum perimeter.

Test yourself answers

1 $\dfrac{-10}{x^3} - 2x$ **2** 9   **3** maximum turning point $(-1, 12)$; minimum turning point $(2, -15)$

4 $\dfrac{-13}{64}$ **5** $y = 5x - 1$ **6** $y = 3x + 6$; $y = 3x + 2$ **7**

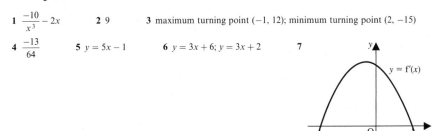

8 Length and breadth both $2\sqrt{3}\,\text{m}$.

7 Polynomials

Key points to remember

1 A **root** of a polynomial function, f(x), is a value of x for which f(x) = 0.

2 When $ax^3 + bx^2 + cx + d$ is divided by $x - h$, the quotient and remainder can be found by synthetic division:

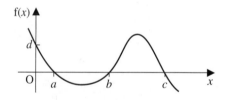

$$\begin{array}{c|cccc}
h & a & b & c & d \\
 & & +h \searrow \; ah & +h \searrow \; ah^2 + bh & +h \searrow \; ah^3 + bh^2 + ch \\
\hline
 & a & ah + b & ah^2 + bh + c & ah^3 + bh^2 + ch + d \; = \text{f}(h)
\end{array}$$

The quotient is $ax^2 + (ah + b)x + (ah^2 + bh + c)$ and the remainder is $ah^3 + bh^2 + ch + d$.

3 The remainder theorem:
If a polynomial f(x) is divided by $(x - h)$ the remainder is f(h).

4 The factor theorem:
If f(h) = 0 then $x - h$ is a factor of f(x).
Conversely, if $(x - h)$ is a factor of f(x) then f(h) = 0.

5 The equation of a polynomial may be established from its graph:

f(x) = $k(x - a)(x - b)(x - c)$ is the general equation for the family of curves. k can be found by substituting $(0, d)$ in f(x).

6 A root of a polynomial lies between $x = a$ and $x = b$
if f(a) > 0 and f(b) < 0 or if f(a) < 0 and f(b) > 0.

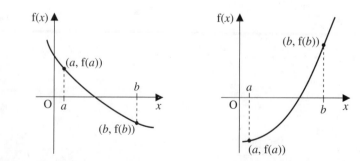

Outcome 1

Use the Factor/Remainder Theorem and apply quadratic theory.
See Chapter 8 for quadratic theory.

Performance criteria

PC(a)   Apply the Factor/Remainder Theorem to a polynomial function.

U Example 1

Show that $(x - 5)$ is a factor of $f(x) = 2x^3 + x^2 - 50x - 25$ and express $f(x)$ in fully factorised form.

Solution

$$
\begin{array}{c|cccc}
5 & 2 & 1 & -50 & -25 \\
  &   & {}^{+5}\!\!\searrow\ 10 & {}^{+5}\!\!\searrow\ 55 & {}^{+5}\!\!\searrow\ 25 \\
\hline
  & 2 & 11 & 5 & 0
\end{array}
\qquad \text{so}\quad f(5) = 0
$$

Since $f(5) = 0$, $(x - 5)$ is a factor of $2x^3 + x^2 - 50x - 25$
Hence $f(x) = (x - 5)(2x^2 + 11x + 5)$
$\qquad\quad = (x - 5)(2x + 1)(x + 5)$

U Example 2

Express $(8x^4 + 2x^2 - 4x - 3) \div (2x - 1)$ in the form
$(2x - 1)Q(x) + R$, where $Q(x)$ is the quotient and R is the remainder.

Solution

$2x - 1 = 0$ has root $x = \frac{1}{2}$

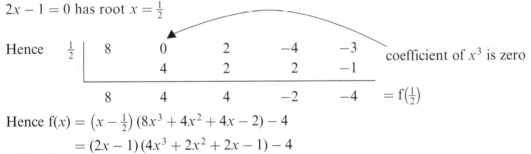

$$
\text{Hence}\quad
\begin{array}{c|ccccc}
\frac{1}{2} & 8 & 0 & 2 & -4 & -3 \\
   &   & 4 & 2 & 2 & -1 \\
\hline
   & 8 & 4 & 4 & -2 & -4
\end{array}
\quad = f\!\left(\tfrac{1}{2}\right)
$$

coefficient of x^3 is zero

Hence $f(x) = \left(x - \frac{1}{2}\right)(8x^3 + 4x^2 + 4x - 2) - 4$
$\qquad\quad = (2x - 1)(4x^3 + 2x^2 + 2x - 1) - 4$

C Example 3

Find the roots of $x^4 + x^3 - 9x^2 - 7x + 14 = 0$.

Solution

To find the roots consider factors of 14, i.e. $\pm 1, \pm 2, \pm 7$

$$
\begin{array}{c|ccccc}
1 & 1 & 1 & -9 & -7 & 14 \\
  &   & 1 & 2 & -7 & -14 \\
\hline
  & 1 & 2 & -7 & -14 & 0
\end{array}
$$

$f(x) = (x - 1)(x^3 + 2x^2 - 7x - 14)$

To find the factors of $(x^3 + 2x^2 - 7x - 14)$:

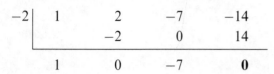

$$-2 \begin{array}{|ccccc} 1 & 2 & -7 & -14 \\ & -2 & 0 & 14 \\ \hline 1 & 0 & -7 & \mathbf{0} \end{array}$$

$f(x) = (x - 1)(x + 2)(x^2 - 7)$

Hence, $x - 1 = 0 \quad$ or $\quad x + 2 = 0 \quad$ or $\quad x^2 - 7 = 0$

$\qquad x = 1 \qquad\qquad x = -2 \qquad\qquad x = \pm\sqrt{7}$

The roots are $-\sqrt{7}, -2, 1, \sqrt{7}$.

C Example 4

Given that $(x + 1)$ and $(x - 3)$ are factors of
$f(x) = 2x^3 - 5x^2 + px + q$, find p and q.

Solution

$$-1 \begin{array}{|cccc} 2 & -5 & p & q \\ & -2 & 7 & -p - 7 \\ \hline 2 & -7 & p + 7 & q - p - 7 = 0 \end{array}$$

$$3 \begin{array}{|cccc} 2 & -5 & p & q \\ & 6 & 3 & 3p + 9 \\ \hline 2 & 1 & p + 3 & q + 3p + 9 = 0 \end{array}$$

Solving simultaneous equations $q - p = 7$ and $q + 3p = -9$ gives
$p = -4$ and $q = 3$.

C Example 5

From the graph find an expression for $f(x)$.

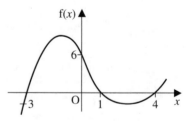

Solution

The graph has zeros at $x = -3$, $x = 1$ and $x = 4$ hence
$f(x) = k(x + 3)(x - 1)(x - 4)$

From the graph, $\qquad f(0) = 6$

so $\quad k(0 + 3)(0 - 1)(0 - 4) = 6$

$\qquad\qquad\qquad\quad 12k = 6$

$\qquad\qquad\qquad\qquad k = \tfrac{1}{2}$

Hence $f(x) = \tfrac{1}{2}(x + 3)(x - 1)(x - 4)$

$\qquad\qquad = \tfrac{1}{2}x^3 - x^2 + \dfrac{11x}{2} + 6$

C   Example 6

Sketch the graph of $y = 3x^3 - 9x + 6$.

Solution

y-intercept

When $x = 0$, $y = 6$ so the y-intercept is at $(0, 6)$.

x-intercept

Solve $3x^3 - 9x + 6 = 0$

$3(x^3 - 3x + 2) = 0$

1	1	0	-3	2
		1	1	-2
	1	1	-2	**0**

$3(x - 1)(x^2 + x - 2) = 0$

$3(x - 1)(x + 2)(x - 1) = 0$

$x - 1 = 0$ or $x + 2 = 0$

$x = 1$ or $x = -2$

The graph cuts the x-axis at $(1, 0)$ and $(-2, 0)$.

Stationary points

$y = 3x^3 - 9x + 6$

$\dfrac{dy}{dx} = 9x^2 - 9$

For stationary points $\dfrac{dy}{dx} = 0$

$9x^2 - 9 = 0$

$9(x + 1)(x - 1) = 0$

$x = -1$ or $x = 1$

When $x = -1$, $y = 12$

When $x = 1$, $y = 0$

x	-1^-	-1	-1^+
$\dfrac{dy}{dx}$	$+$	0	$-$
slope	/	—	\

x	1^-	1	1^+
$\dfrac{dy}{dx}$	$-$	0	$+$
slope	\	—	/

maximum turning point $(-1, 12)$ minimum turning point $(1, 0)$

Large positive and negative x   *Graph*

As $x \to -\infty$, $3x^3 - 9x + 6 \to x^3 \to -\infty$

As $x \to \infty$, $3x^3 - 9x + 6 \to x^3 \to \infty$

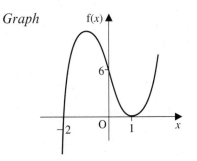

C Example 7

For the function $f(x) = x^3 - x^2 + 2x + 1$ show there is a real root between 0 and -1. Find this root to two decimal places.

Solution

$f(0) = 1$, which is positive so the graph is above the x-axis.

$f(-1) = -3$, which is negative so the graph is below the x-axis.

Hence the graph crosses the x-axis between 0 and -1.

Evaluate $f(x)$ for values between 0 and -1.

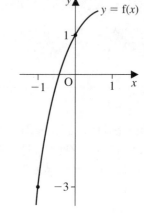

x	$f(x)$	Root lies between
0	1	
-1	-3	0 and -1
-0.3	0.283	-1 and -0.3
-0.4	-0.024	-0.3 and -0.4
-0.38	0.0407	-0.38 and -0.4
-0.39	0.00858	-0.39 and -0.4
-0.395	-0.00765	-0.39 and -0.395

The root is -0.39 to two decimal places.

Revision exercise 7

U 1 Show that $(x + 3)$ is a factor of $f(x) = 2x^3 + 5x^2 - 4x - 3$ and express $f(x)$ in fully factorised form.

U 2 Factorise fully
(a) $x^3 - 8x^2 + 19x - 12$
(b) $2x^3 + 7x^2 + 2x - 3$.

U 3 Show that -2 is a root of the equation $8 - x^3 - x^4 = 0$.

U 4 Find the roots of $(1 - x^2)(4x + x^3) = 0$.

U 5 Find the quotient and remainder when
(a) $x^3 + 2x^2 - 3x + 4$ is divided by $(x - 5)$
(b) $3x^3 - 7x^2 + 5x + 4$ is divided by $(x + 3)$.

C 6 Given that $(x + 3)$ is a factor of $f(x) = 2x^3 - 3x^2 + kx - 15$, find the value of k and factorise $f(x)$ fully when k has this value.

C 7 Given that $2x - 1$ is a factor of $8x^3 + 4x^2 + kx + 15$, find the value of k and factorise $f(x)$ fully when k has this value.

C 8 For each function find (i) c for the given zero and (ii) the other zeros of the function.
(a) $y = 2x^3 - x^2 + cx - 6$, zero at $x = 3$
(b) $y = 3x^3 + cx^2 - 12x + 4$, zero at $x = -2$

C 9 Find the values of a and b if $(x - 3)$ and $(x + 2)$ are factors of $x^3 + ax^2 + bx + 42$.

C 10 Given that $f(x) = x^3 + ax^2 + bx - 1$ and $f(1) = 3b$, calculate the ratio $a:b$.

C **11** If $x + 1$ is a factor of $px^3 + qx^2 + px + q$ show that $p = q$.

C **12** From the graph determine the function $y = f(x)$.

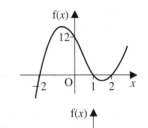

C **13** From the graph find an expression for the function $f(x)$.

C **14** The graph of a cubic function crosses the x-axis at 1, -5 and -3. It crosses the y-axis at -5. Find the equation of the function.

C **15** Sketch the curve $y = 8 + 2x^2 - x^4$.

C **16** (a) Sketch the graph of $y = x^3 + x^2 - x - 1$.
(b) Solve $x^3 + x^2 - x - 1 < 0$.

C **17** (a) Show that $x^3 - 2x = 5$ has a root between 2 and 3.
(b) Find the root to two decimal places.

C **18** Show that $x^3 - x^2 - 2x + 1 = 0$ has a root between 1 and 2, and find the root to two decimal places.

C **19** The line $y = 1 - 2x$ intersects $y = 3x - x^3$ between $x = 0$ and $x = 1$. Find the x-coordinate of the point of intersection, to one decimal place.

Test yourself	What to review
	If your answer is incorrect:
U **1** Show that $(x - 3)$ is a factor of $f(x) = x^3 - 8x^2 + 19x - 12$ and express $f(x)$ in fully factorised form.	*Review Heinemann Higher Mathematics Chapter 7, pages 130 and 131*
U **2** Factorise fully $2x^3 + 7x^2 + 2x - 3$.	*Review Heinemann Higher Mathematics Chapter 7, pages 130 and 131*
C **3** Find p if $(x + 2)$ is a factor of $x^3 + px^2 - x - 2$.	*Review Heinemann Higher Mathematics Chapter 7, page 132*
C **4** From the graph find an expression for $f(x)$. 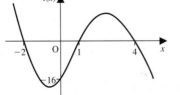	*Review Heinemann Higher Mathematics Chapter 7, pages 134 and 135*

C 5 Sketch the curve $y = x^3 - 3x - 2$.

Review Heinemann Higher Mathematics Chapter 7, pages 136 and 137

C 6 Show that $x^3 - 4x + 2 = 0$ has a root between 0 and 1, and find the root to two decimal places.

Review Heinemann Higher Mathematics Chapter 7, pages 137 and 138

Test yourself answers

1 $f(x) = (x - 3)(x - 1)(x - 4)$ **2** $(2x - 1)(x + 3)(x + 1)$ **3** 2   **4** $f(x) = -2x^3 + 6x^2 + 12x - 16$

5

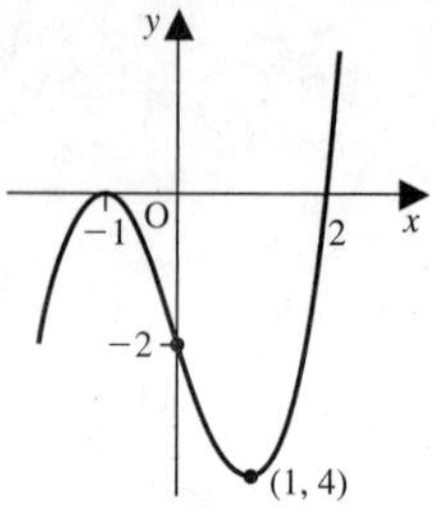

6 0.54

8 Quadratic functions

Key points to remember

1 The graph of a quadratic function $y = ax^2 + bx + c$ is a **parabola**.
If $a > 0$ the parabola is $\smile$ shaped and the turning point is a minimum.
If $a < 0$ the parabola is $\frown$ shaped and the turning point is a maximum.

2 To sketch and anotate a parabola $y = ax^2 + bx + c$ we
need to identify where possible:
- whether the shape is $\smile$ $(a > 0)$ or $\frown$ $(a < 0)$
- the coordinates of the y-intercept, $(0, c)$
- the zeros of the function by solving $ax^2 + bx + c = 0$
- the equation of the axis of symmetry
- the coordinates of the turning point.

3 When the equation $y = ax^2 + bx + c$ is written
in the form $y = a(x + p)^2 + q$, the axis of
symmetry is $x = -p$ and the turning point is
at $(-p, q)$.

4 Quadratic equations may be solved by
- using the graph
- factorising
- completing the square
- using the quadratic formula.

5 A quadratic inequation can be
solved using a sketch of the
quadratic function.

6 If $ax^2 + bx + c = 0$ then $x = \dfrac{-b \pm \sqrt{b^2 - 4ac}}{2a}$ where $a \neq 0$

7 For the quadratic equation $ax^2 + bx + c = 0$, $b^2 - 4ac$ is called the **discriminant**:
(i) if $b^2 - 4ac > 0$, the roots are real and unequal
(ii) if $b^2 - 4ac = 0$, the roots are real and equal
(iii) if $b^2 - 4ac < 0$, the roots are non-real.

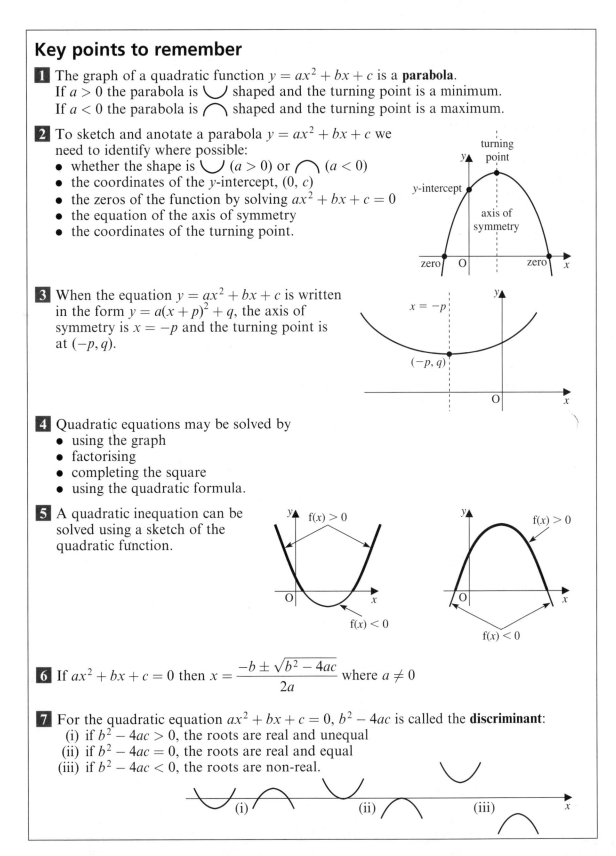

8 For a quadratic equation formed when the equation of a straight line is substituted into the equation of a parabola:
  (i) if $b^2 - 4ac > 0$, the line intersects the curve at two places
  (ii) if $b^2 - 4ac = 0$, the line is a tangent to the curve
  (iii) if $b^2 - 4ac < 0$, the line does not intersect the curve.

Outcome 1

Use the Factor/Remainder Theorem and apply quadratic theory.
See Chapter 7 for Factor/Remainder Theorem.

Performance criteria

PC(b) Determine the nature of the roots of a quadratic equation using the discriminant.

U Example 1

Determine the nature of the roots of each of these equations, using the discriminant.
  (a) $x^2 - 6x + 8 = 0$ (b) $x^2 - 6x + 9 = 0$ (c) $x^2 - 6x + 10 = 0$

Solution

(a) $x^2 - 6x + 8 = 0$ $a = 1, b = -6, c = 8$
  $b^2 - 4ac = (-6)^2 - (4 \times 1 \times 8) = 36 - 32 = 4$

  discriminant is positive, so there are two unequal (distinct) real roots.

(b) $x^2 - 6x + 9 = 0$ $a = 1, b = -6, c = 9$
  $b^2 - 4ac = (-6)^2 - (4 \times 1 \times 9) = 36 - 36 = 0$

  discriminant is zero, so roots are real and equal.

(c) $x^2 - 6x + 10 = 0$ $a = 1, b = -6, c = 10$
  $b^2 - 4ac = (-6)^2 - (4 \times 1 \times 10) = 36 - 40 = -4$

  discriminant is negative, so roots are non-real.

C Example 2

For what values of p does the equation $x^2 - 2px + (2 - p) = 0$ have non-real roots?

Solution

$x^2 - 2px + (2 - p) = 0$

$a = 1, b = -2p, c = 2 - p$

For non-real roots $b^2 - 4ac < 0$, so

$(-2p)^2 - 4(2 - p) < 0$
$4p^2 - 8 + 4p < 0$
$4(p^2 + p - 2) < 0$
$4(p - 1)(p + 2) < 0$

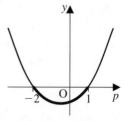

From the graph of $4(p - 1)(p + 2) < 0$ when $-2 < p < 1$
The equation has non-real roots when $-2 < p < 1$

C Example 3

Find values of q so that $\dfrac{1}{x^2 - x + 1} = q$ has two equal roots.

Solution

Cross-multiplying gives $q(x^2 - x + 1) = 1$
$$qx^2 - qx + q = 1$$
$$qx^2 - qx + (q - 1) = 0$$
$$a = q,\ b = -q,\ c = (q - 1)$$

For equal roots $b^2 - 4ac = 0$, so
$$(-q)^2 - 4q(q - 1) = 0$$
$$q^2 - 4q^2 + 4q = 0$$
$$4q - 3q^2 = 0$$
$$q(4 - 3q) = 0$$

The equation has two equal roots when $q = 0$ or $q = \frac{4}{3}$.

C Example 4

Given that k is a real number, show that the roots of the equation $kx^2 + 5x + 5 = k$ are always real numbers.

Solution

$$kx^2 + 5x + 5 = k$$
$$kx^2 + 5x + (5 - k) = 0$$
$$a = k,\ b = 5,\ c = 5 - k$$
$$b^2 - 4ac = 25 - 4k(5 - k)$$
$$= 25 - 20k + 4k^2$$
$$= (5 - 2k)^2$$

Since $(5 - 2k)^2$ is a square it has a minimum value zero, therefore $b^2 - 4ac \geqslant 0$ and so the roots of the equation are always real.

C Example 5

Find the equation of the parabola that passes through $(-1, 0)$, $(5, 0)$ and $(0, -10)$ in the form $y = ax^2 + bx + c$.

Solution

The parabola cuts the x-axis at $x = -1$ and $x = 5$,

so $k(x + 1)(x - 5) = 0$, where k is a constant
$$y = k(x + 1)(x - 5)$$

When $x = 0$, $y = -10$
$$k(0 + 1)(0 - 5) = -10$$
$$-5k = -10$$
$$k = 2$$

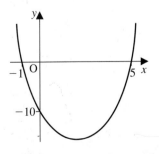

Hence $y = 2(x + 1)(x - 5) = 2x^2 - 8x - 10$

C Example 6

Show that $y = 15 - 7x$ is a tangent to the parabola
$y = -x^2 - x + 6$ and find the point of contact.

Solution

The line and parabola meet where $15 - 7x = -x^2 - x + 6$
$$x^2 - 6x + 9 = 0$$

$b^2 - 4ac = (-6)^2 - (4 \times 1 \times 9) = 0$

so there is one point of intersection. Hence the line is
a tangent to the parabola.

The line and parabola meet where $x^2 - 6x + 9 = 0$
$$(x - 3)(x - 3) = 0$$
$$\text{so } x = 3$$

The point of contact is $(3, -6)$.

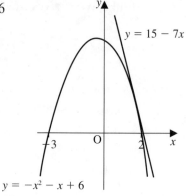

C Example 7

The line $y = -2x + k$ is a tangent to the parabola $y = 4x - x^2$.
Find the value of k.

Solution

$y = -2x + k$ meets $y = 4x - x^2$ where $-2x + k = 4x - x^2$
$$x^2 - 6x + k = 0$$

Tangency implies equal roots therefore $b^2 - 4ac = 0$
$$(-6)^2 - 4k = 0$$
$$k = 9$$

The equation of the tangent is $y = 9 - 2x$.

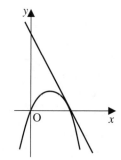

Revision exercise 8

U 1 Use the discriminant to determine the nature of the roots of
the equations:
(a) $2x^2 - 6x + 5 = 0$ (b) $3x^2 + 4x - 7 = 0$
(c) $4x^2 - 28x + 49 = 0$

U 2 Show algebraically that
(a) $x^2 - 10x + 24 = 0$ has two real roots
(b) $x^2 - 10x + 25 = 0$ has one real root
(c) $x^2 - 10x + 26 = 0$ has no real roots.

C 3 For each parabola state its equation in the form $y = ax^2 + bx + c$.

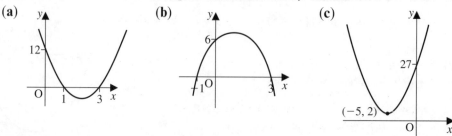

C   4   Find the real values of x satisfying
   (a) $(2x - 1)(x + 3) < 0$ **(b)** $2x^2 - x - 3 > 0$
   (c) $15 < x(2x + 7)$

C   5   For each equation find the value(s) of p so that the roots
   are equal
   (a) $4x^2 - px + 1 = 0$ **(b)** $px^2 + px + (p - 1) = 0$

C   6   For what values of k does each equation have non-real
   roots?
   (a) $kx^2 + 5x - 1 = 0$ **(b)** $kx^2 - 8x + k = 0$

C   7   Find the value of k for which the equation $2x^2 + 4x + k = 0$
   has real roots.   [Higher]

C   8   Find the values of k for which the quadratic equation in x,
   $x^2 - 2x + 21 = 2k(3x - 7)$, has equal roots.   [Higher]

C   9   Show that the roots of each of the following equations are
   always real
   (a) $kx^2 + (k - 2)x - 1 = 0$ **(b)** $(k - 1)x^2 + kx + 1 = 0$

C   10 x is a real number and $k = \dfrac{x^2 + 4x + 10}{2x + 5}$. By considering a
   quadratic equation in x, show that k cannot have a value
   between -3 and 2.   [Higher]

C   11   If p and q are real, show that each of the following
   equations always has real roots
   (a) $qx^2 + px - q = 0$ **(b)** $x^2 + (q - p)x - pq = 0$
   (c) $2px^2 + (p + 2q)x + q = 0$

C   12   Calculate the least positive integer value of k so that the
   graph of $y = kx^2 - 6x + k$ does not cut or touch the x-axis.

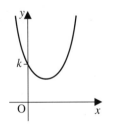

C   13   Show that the line with equation $y = 1 - x$ is a tangent to
   the parabola $y = x^2 - 3x + 2$ and state the coordinates of
   the point of contact.

C   14   Prove that the line $y = 5x - 6$ is a tangent to the parabola
   $y = 4x^2 - 15x + 19$.

C   15   The line $y = mx + 8$ is a tangent to $y = x^2 + 9$. Find two
   values for m.

C   16   Find the equation of the tangent to the parabola
   $y = 4x - x^2$ with gradient 2.

Test yourself	What to review
	If your answer is incorrect:
U 1 Use the discriminant to determine the nature of the roots of the equation $3x^2 - 5x - 4 = 0$.	*Review Heinemann Higher Mathematics Chapter 8, page 151*
U 2 Show that the quadratic equation $5x^2 - 2x + 7 = 0$ has no real roots.	*Review Heinemann Higher Mathematics Chapter 8, page 151*
C 3 Find q given that $x^2 - 2x + q = 0$ has non-real roots.	*Review Heinemann Higher Mathematics Chapter 8, page 152*
C 4 The roots of the equation $(x - 1)(x + k) = -4$ are equal. Find the value(s) of k.	*Review Heinemann Higher Mathematics, Chapter 8, page 152*
C 5 Given that p is a real number show that the roots of $(p - 1)x^2 + px + 1 = 0$ are always real.	*Review Heinemann Higher Mathematics, Chapter 8, page 152*
C 6 Find the real values of x satisfying $x^2 - x - 2 < 0$.	*Review Heinemann Higher Mathematics, Chapter 8, page 148*
C 7 If $\dfrac{(x - 2)^2}{x^2 + 2} = k$, where k is a real number, find values of k such that the given equation has non-real roots.	*Review Heinemann Higher Mathematics, Chapter 8, page 152*
C 8 Show that the line with equation $y = 4x - 1$ is a tangent to the parabola with equation $y = x^2 + 6x$.	*Review Heinemann Higher Mathematics, Chapter 8, page 154*
C 9 Find k such that the line $y = -2x + k$ is a tangent to the parabola $y = x^2 + 4x$ and find the coordinates of the point of contact.	*Review Heinemann Higher Mathematics, Chapter 8, page 154*

Test yourself answers

1 $b^2 - 4ac = 73$, real roots   **2** $b^2 - 4ac = -136$ **3** $q > 1$ **4** $-5, 3$ **5** $b^2 - 4ac = (p - 2)^2$
6 $-1 < x < 2$ **7** $k < 0, k > 3$ **9** $-9, (-3, -3)$

9 Integration

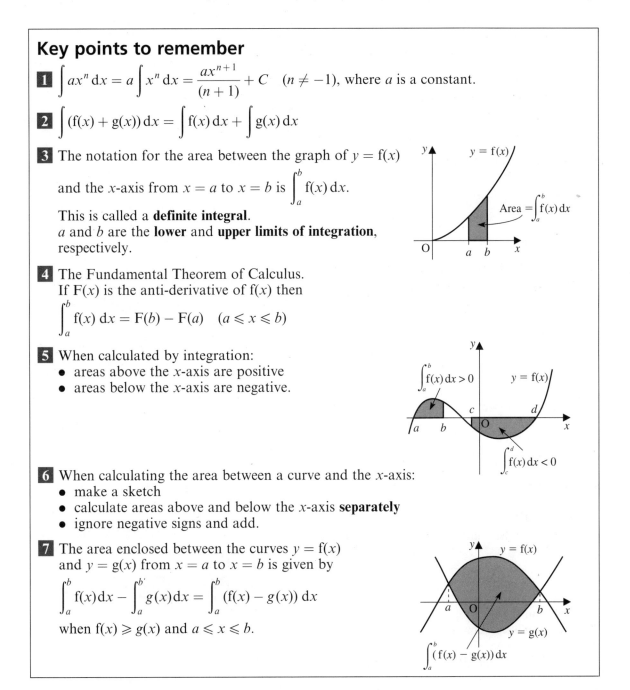

Key points to remember

1 $\int ax^n \, dx = a \int x^n \, dx = \dfrac{ax^{n+1}}{(n+1)} + C \quad (n \neq -1)$, where a is a constant.

2 $\int (f(x) + g(x)) \, dx = \int f(x) \, dx + \int g(x) \, dx$

3 The notation for the area between the graph of $y = f(x)$ and the x-axis from $x = a$ to $x = b$ is $\displaystyle\int_a^b f(x) \, dx$.

This is called a **definite integral**.
a and b are the **lower** and **upper limits of integration**, respectively.

4 The Fundamental Theorem of Calculus.
If $F(x)$ is the anti-derivative of $f(x)$ then

$$\int_a^b f(x) \, dx = F(b) - F(a) \quad (a \leqslant x \leqslant b)$$

5 When calculated by integration:
- areas above the x-axis are positive
- areas below the x-axis are negative.

6 When calculating the area between a curve and the x-axis:
- make a sketch
- calculate areas above and below the x-axis **separately**
- ignore negative signs and add.

7 The area enclosed between the curves $y = f(x)$ and $y = g(x)$ from $x = a$ to $x = b$ is given by

$$\int_a^b f(x) \, dx - \int_a^b g(x) \, dx = \int_a^b (f(x) - g(x)) \, dx$$

when $f(x) \geqslant g(x)$ and $a \leqslant x \leqslant b$.

Outcome 2

Use basic integration.

Performance criteria

PC(a)   Integrate functions reducible to the sums of powers of x (definite and indefinite).

PC(b)   Find the area between a curve and the x-axis using integration.

PC(c)   Find the area between two curves using integration.

U Example 1

Integrate $\displaystyle\int \sqrt{x} - \frac{2}{x^3}\,\mathrm{d}x$

Solution

$$\int \sqrt{x} - \frac{2}{x^3}\,\mathrm{d}x$$

$$= \int x^{\frac{1}{2}} - 2x^{-3}\,\mathrm{d}x$$

$$= \frac{x^{\frac{3}{2}}}{\frac{3}{2}} - \frac{2x^{-2}}{-2} + C$$

$$= \frac{2x^{\frac{3}{2}}}{3} + \frac{1}{x^2} + C$$

U Example 2

Integrate $\displaystyle\int \frac{4x - x^{\frac{3}{2}}}{2\sqrt{x}}\,\mathrm{d}x$

Solution

$$\int \frac{4x - x^{\frac{3}{2}}}{2\sqrt{x}}\,\mathrm{d}x$$

$$= \int \frac{4x}{2x^{\frac{1}{2}}} - \frac{x^{\frac{3}{2}}}{2x^{\frac{1}{2}}}\,\mathrm{d}x$$

$$= \int 2x^{\frac{1}{2}} - \frac{x}{2}\,\mathrm{d}x$$

$$= \frac{2x^{\frac{3}{2}}}{\frac{3}{2}} - \frac{x^2}{4} + C$$

$$= \frac{4x^{\frac{3}{2}}}{3} - \frac{x^2}{4} + C$$

U Example 3

Evaluate $\displaystyle\int_1^2 (3x - 1)(x + 5)\,\mathrm{d}x$

Solution

$$\int_1^2 (3x - 1)(x + 5)\,\mathrm{d}x$$

$$= \int_1^2 3x^2 + 14x - 5\,\mathrm{d}x$$

$$= \left[x^3 + 7x^2 - 5x\right]_1^2$$

$$= (8 + 28 - 10) - (1 + 7 - 5)$$

$$= 23$$

U Example 4

Calculate the shaded area in the diagram.

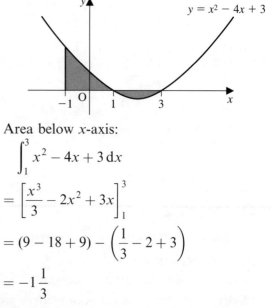

$$y = x^2 - 4x + 3$$

Solution
Area above x-axis:

$$\int_{-1}^{1} x^2 - 4x + 3\,\mathrm{d}x$$

$$= \left[\frac{x^3}{3} - 2x^2 + 3x\right]_{-1}^{1}$$

$$= \left(\frac{1}{3} - 2 + 3\right) - \left(\frac{-1}{3} - 2 - 3\right)$$

$$= 6\frac{2}{3}$$

Total area $= 6\dfrac{2}{3} + 1\dfrac{1}{3} = 8$ units^2

Area below x-axis:

$$\int_{1}^{3} x^2 - 4x + 3\,\mathrm{d}x$$

$$= \left[\frac{x^3}{3} - 2x^2 + 3x\right]_{1}^{3}$$

$$= (9 - 18 + 9) - \left(\frac{1}{3} - 2 + 3\right)$$

$$= -1\frac{1}{3}$$

Note: Ignore negative sign for area below the x-axis.

U **Example 5**

Find the area enclosed by $y = x^2 - x - 2$ and the x-axis.

Solution

The graph cuts the x-axis when $x^2 - x - 2 = 0$

$$(x+1)(x-2) = 0$$

$$\text{so} \quad x = -1 \quad \text{or} \quad x = 2$$

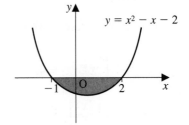

Area: $\displaystyle\int_{-1}^{2} x^2 - x - 2 \, dx$

$$= \left[\frac{x^3}{3} - \frac{x^2}{2} - 2x \right]_{-1}^{2}$$

$$= \left(\frac{8}{3} - 2 - 4 \right) - \left(-\frac{1}{3} - \frac{1}{2} + 2 \right)$$

$$= -4\frac{1}{2}$$

So the area is $4\dfrac{1}{2}$ units^2

U **Example 6**

Find the area enclosed by the graphs of $y = x + 1$ and $y = 5 - 2x - x^2$.

Solution

The graphs intersect where $x + 1 = 5 - 2x - x^2$

$$x + 3x - 4 = 0$$

$$(x+4)(x-1) = 0$$

$$\text{so} \quad x = -4 \quad \text{or} \quad x = 1$$

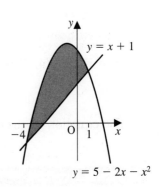

Area: $\displaystyle\int_{-4}^{1} (5 - 2x - x^2) - (x + 1) \, dx$

$$= \int_{-4}^{1} 4 - 3x - x^2 \, dx$$

$$= \left[4x - \frac{3x^2}{2} - \frac{x^3}{3} \right]_{-4}^{1}$$

$$= \left(4 - \frac{3}{2} - \frac{1}{3} \right) - \left(-16 - 24 + \frac{64}{3} \right)$$

$$= 20\frac{5}{6} \text{ units}^2$$

C **Example 7**
Determine p given that $\int_1^p \sqrt{x}\,dx = 42$.   [Higher]

Solution

$$\int_1^p \sqrt{x}\,dx = 42$$

$$\int_1^p x^{\frac{1}{2}}\,dx = 42$$

$$\left[\frac{2x^{\frac{3}{2}}}{3}\right]_1^p = 42$$

$$\left(\frac{2p^{\frac{3}{2}}}{3}\right) - \left(\frac{2}{3}\right) = 42$$

$$\frac{2p^{\frac{3}{2}}}{3} = \frac{128}{3}$$

$$p^{\frac{3}{2}} = 64$$

$$p = 16$$

C **Example 8**
The gradient of a tangent to a curve is given by $\dfrac{dy}{dx} = \dfrac{1}{2\sqrt{x}}$.

If the curve passes through the point (4, 3) find its
equation.   [Higher]

Solution

$$y = \int \frac{1}{2\sqrt{x}}\,dx = \int \frac{x^{-\frac{1}{2}}}{2}\,dx$$

$$= x^{\frac{1}{2}} + C$$

$$= \sqrt{x} + C$$

Substituting (4, 3) in $y = \sqrt{x} + C$
$$3 = \sqrt{4} + C$$
$$C = 1$$
The equation of the curve is $y = \sqrt{x} + 1$

Revision exercise 9

U **1** Integrate

(a) $\displaystyle\int x^3 + \frac{1}{\sqrt{x}}\,dx$ (b) $\displaystyle\int (5 + 3x)^2\,dx$ (c) $\displaystyle\int \frac{x^3 - 5x}{\sqrt{x}}\,dx$

U **2** Evaluate

(a) $\displaystyle\int_1^2 \frac{dx}{x^2}$ (b) $\displaystyle\int_1^4 \sqrt{x} + x\,dx$ (c) $\displaystyle\int_{-1}^3 \frac{x - x^3}{x}\,dx$

U 3 Calculate the shaded area in each graph.

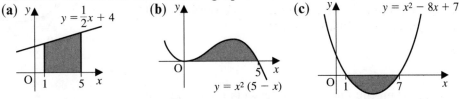

(a) $y = \frac{1}{2}x + 4$

(b) $y = x^2(5 - x)$

(c) $y = x^2 - 8x + 7$

U 4 Without carrying out the integration, write the integral which represents the shaded area in each graph.

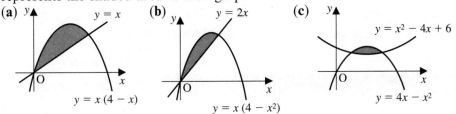

(a) $y = x$ $y = x(4 - x)$

(b) $y = 2x$ $y = x(4 - x^2)$

(c) $y = x^2 - 4x + 6$ $y = 4x - x^2$

U 5 For each of the following (i) evaluate the integral and (ii) draw a sketch to illustrate the integral as an area.

(a) $\displaystyle\int_{-2}^{3} 2x + 5 \, dx$ (b) $\displaystyle\int_{1}^{4} 4 - x \, dx$ (c) $\displaystyle\int_{1}^{2} 3x^2 + 4 \, dx$

[Higher]

U 6 Calculate the area enclosed by the following curves and the x-axis.

(a) $y = (4 - x)(1 + x)$ (b) $y = x^2 + x - 12$ (c) $y = x^2(x - 3)$

U 7 Find the area enclosed by the graphs of
(a) $y = x^2 - 3x$ and $y = x - 3$
(b) $y = 5 + 4x - x^2$ and $y = x^2 - 2x + 5$

C 8 Find the value of

(a) $\displaystyle\int_{1}^{4} \frac{3x + 1}{\sqrt{x}} \, dx$ (b) $\displaystyle\int_{1}^{2} \frac{u^2 + 2}{2u^4} \, du$ (c) $\displaystyle\int_{1}^{9} \frac{x + 1}{\sqrt{x}} \, dx$

[Higher]

C 9 Find the positive value of p for which:

(a) $\displaystyle\int_{0}^{p} 2x + 3 \, dx = 4$ (b) $\displaystyle\int_{0}^{p} \sqrt{x} \, dx = \frac{16}{3}$ (c) $\displaystyle\int_{1}^{p} \frac{dx}{x^2} = \frac{2}{3}$

C 10 A curve for which $\dfrac{dy}{dx} = 3x^2 + 1$ passes through the point $(-1, 2)$. Express y in terms of x.   [Higher]

C 11 A designer has sketched the cover of a stunt kite on a coordinate diagram with the boundaries as described by the given equations. Calculate its area.

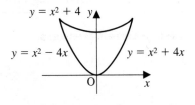

$y = x^2 + 4$

$y = x^2 - 4x$

$y = x^2 + 4x$

C 12 A jeweller has sketched the outline of an earring on a coordinate diagram with boundaries as described by the given equations. Calculate its area.

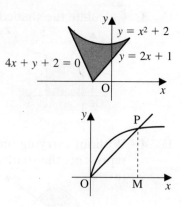

$y = x^2 + 2$
$y = 2x + 1$
$4x + y + 2 = 0$

C 13 In the diagram, the line $y = x$ intersects the curve with equation $y = 2\sqrt{x}$ at O and P. MP is the ordinate at P.
(a) Find the coordinates of P.
(b) Show that the area of triangle OMP is $\frac{3}{4}$ of the area bounded by the arc OP and the lines OM and MP.

[Higher]

Test yourself	**What to review**
	If your answer is incorrect:
U 1 Find $\int \sqrt{x} - \dfrac{2}{x^3}\,\mathrm{d}x$	*Review Heinemann Higher Mathematics Chapter 9, pages 163 to 166*
U 2 Evaluate $\displaystyle\int_1^3 \dfrac{x^3 + 3}{x^2}\,\mathrm{d}x$	*Review Heinemann Higher Mathematics Chapter 9, pages 168 to 169*
U 3 Calculate the shaded area in the diagram. $\quad y = 5 + 4x - x^2$	*Review Heinemann Higher Mathematics Chapter 9, pages 166 to 168*
C 4 Find the area enclosed between the curve $y = 4 - x^2$ and the line $y = 3x$.	*Review Heinemann Higher Mathematics Chapter 9, pages 173 to 175*
C 5 Evaluate $\displaystyle\int_{-1}^1 x^{\frac{1}{2}}\left(2x^{\frac{1}{2}} + 3x^{\frac{3}{2}}\right)\mathrm{d}x$	*Review Heinemann Higher Mathematics Chapter 9, pages 169*
C 6 If $\displaystyle\int_0^p (x - 1)^2\,\mathrm{d}x = 3$ find p.	*Review Heinemann Higher Mathematics Chapter 9, pages 169*
C 7 The gradient of a tangent to a curve is given by $\dfrac{\mathrm{d}y}{\mathrm{d}x} = 3x^2 - 2$. If the curve passes through the point $(1, -2)$ find its equation.	*Review Heinemann Higher Mathematics Chapter 9, pages 175 to 177*

Test yourself answers

1 $\dfrac{2x^{\frac{3}{2}}}{3} + \dfrac{1}{x^2}$ **2** 6   **3** 36   **4** $20\frac{5}{6}$ **5** 2   **6** 3   **7** $y = x^3 - 2x - 1$

10 3-D trigonometry

There are no specific outcomes or performance criteria for this topic and therefore a separate revision chapter is not required.

Questions involving the use of 3-D trigonometry are included in other chapters of this book.

11 Addition formulae

Key points to remember

1 $\sin(\alpha + \beta) = \sin \alpha \cos \beta + \cos \alpha \sin \beta$

2 $\sin(\alpha - \beta) = \sin \alpha \cos \beta - \cos \alpha \sin \beta$

3 $\cos(\alpha + \beta) = \cos \alpha \cos \beta - \sin \alpha \sin \beta$

4 $\cos(\alpha - \beta) = \cos \alpha \cos \beta + \sin \alpha \sin \beta$

5 $\sin 2\alpha = 2 \sin \alpha \cos \alpha$

6 $\cos 2\alpha = \cos^2 \alpha - \sin^2 \alpha$
$\qquad\quad = 2 \cos^2 \alpha - 1$
$\qquad\quad = 1 - 2 \sin^2 \alpha$

7 $\cos^2 \alpha = \frac{1}{2}(1 + \cos 2\alpha)$

8 $\sin^2 \alpha = \frac{1}{2}(1 - \cos 2\alpha)$

Outcome 3

Solve trigonometric equations and apply trigonometric formulae.

Performance criteria

PC(a) Solve a trigonometric equation in a given interval.
PC(b) Apply a trigonometric formula (addition formula) in the solution of a geometric problem.
PC(c) Solve a trigonometric equation involving an addition formula in a given interval.

U Example 1

Solve algebraically $2 \sin 2x° + 1 = 0$ where $0 \leqslant x \leqslant 360$.

Solution
$2 \sin 2x° + 1 = 0$

$\qquad 2 \sin 2x° = -1$

$\qquad\quad \sin 2x° = -\dfrac{1}{2}$

Since $\sin 2x°$ is negative the solutions are in the
third and fourth quadrants.

Also, since $0 \leqslant x \leqslant 360$ then $0 \leqslant 2x \leqslant 720$

$2x = 210$ or 330 or $(210 + 360)$ or $(330 + 360)$

$x = 105$ or 165 or 295 or 345

S	A
T	C
✓	✓

U Example 2

The diagram shows the cross-section of an adjustable ramp which is made from two right-angled triangles, PQR and RQS. Angle RQS = $a°$ and PQR = $b°$.
(a) Find the exact value of $\sin(a + b)°$.
(b) Hence calculate the height of the ramp.

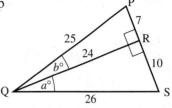

Solution

(a) $\sin(a + b)° = \sin a° \cos b° + \cos a° \sin b°$

$$= \frac{10}{26} \times \frac{24}{25} + \frac{24}{26} \times \frac{7}{25}$$

$$= \frac{240 + 168}{650}$$

$$= \frac{408}{650}$$

(b) $\sin(a + b)° = \dfrac{h}{25}$

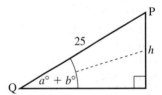

$$h = 25 \sin(a + b)°$$

$$h = 25 \times \frac{408}{650}$$

$$h = 15.69 \, \text{m}$$

U Example 3

(a) Express $\cos x \cos \dfrac{\pi}{6} - \sin x \sin \dfrac{\pi}{6}$ in the form $\cos(A + B)$.

(b) Hence solve the equation $\cos x \cos \dfrac{\pi}{6} - \sin x \sin \dfrac{\pi}{6} = \dfrac{1}{2}$

for $0 \leqslant x \leqslant 2\pi$.

Solution

(a) $\cos x \cos \dfrac{\pi}{6} - \sin x \sin \dfrac{\pi}{6} = \cos\left(x + \dfrac{\pi}{6}\right)$

(b) $\cos x \cos \dfrac{\pi}{6} - \sin x \sin \dfrac{\pi}{6} = \dfrac{1}{2}$

$$\cos\left(x + \frac{\pi}{6}\right) = \frac{1}{2}$$

$$x + \frac{\pi}{6} = \frac{\pi}{3} \text{ or } \frac{5\pi}{3}$$

$$x = \frac{\pi}{3} - \frac{\pi}{6} \text{ or } \frac{5\pi}{3} - \frac{\pi}{6}$$

$$x = \frac{\pi}{6} \text{ or } \frac{3\pi}{2}$$

S	A ✓
T	C ✓

C   Example 4

Find the exact value of $\cos 15°$.

Solution

$$\cos 15° = \cos(45 - 30)°$$

$$= \cos 45° \cos 30° + \sin 45° \sin 30°$$

$$= \frac{1}{\sqrt{2}} \times \frac{\sqrt{3}}{2} + \frac{1}{\sqrt{2}} \times \frac{1}{2}$$

$$= \frac{\sqrt{3}}{2\sqrt{2}} + \frac{1}{2\sqrt{2}}$$

$$= \frac{(\sqrt{3}+1)}{2\sqrt{2}}$$

C   Example 5

The diagram shows the graphs of
$f(x) = 3\sin x - 1$ and $g(x) = \cos 2x$ for
$0 \leqslant x \leqslant \pi$.

(a)   Solve algebraically the equation
$3\sin x - 1 = \cos 2x$.

(b)   Hence find the coordinates of A and B.

(c)   For what values of x in the interval
$0 \leqslant x \leqslant \pi$ is $\cos 2x \leqslant 3\sin x - 1$?

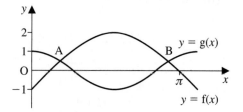

Solution

(a) $$3\sin x - 1 = \cos 2x$$

$$3\sin x - 1 = 1 - 2\sin^2 x$$

$$2\sin^2 x + 3\sin x - 2 = 0$$

$$(2\sin x - 1)(\sin x + 2) = 0$$

$$\sin x = \frac{1}{2} \text{ or } \sin x = -2$$

$$x = \frac{\pi}{6}, \frac{5\pi}{6} \text{ (as } \sin x = -2 \text{ has no solution)}$$

(b)   When $x = \dfrac{\pi}{6}$, $g(x) = \cos \dfrac{\pi}{3} = \dfrac{1}{2}$, so A is $\left(\dfrac{\pi}{6}, \dfrac{1}{2}\right)$

When $x = \dfrac{5\pi}{6}$, $g(x) = \cos \dfrac{5\pi}{3} = \dfrac{1}{2}$, so B is $\left(\dfrac{5\pi}{6}, \dfrac{1}{2}\right)$

(c)   For the interval $0 \leqslant x \leqslant \pi$, $g(x)$ lies below $f(x)$ when

$$\frac{\pi}{6} \leqslant x \leqslant \frac{5\pi}{6}$$

C Example 6

Solve $3\cos 2x° = \cos x° - 1$, for $0 \leqslant x \leqslant 360$.   [Higher]

Solution

$$3\cos 2x° = \cos x° - 1$$
$$3(2\cos^2 x° - 1) = \cos x° - 1$$
$$6\cos^2 x° - 3 - \cos x° + 1 = 0$$
$$6\cos^2 x° - \cos x° - 2 = 0$$
$$(2\cos x° + 1)(3\cos x° - 2) = 0$$
$$2\cos x° + 1 = 0 \text{ or } 3\cos x° - 2 = 0$$
$$\cos x° = -\tfrac{1}{2} \text{ or } \cos x° = \tfrac{2}{3}$$
$$x = 120, \ 240 \text{ or } x = 48.2, \ 311.8$$

C Example 7

The diagram shows an isosceles triangle KLM in which
KL = KM and angle KLM = $x°$.

(a) Show that $\dfrac{\sin x°}{m} = \dfrac{\sin 2x°}{k}$

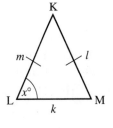

(b) (i) State the value of x when $k = m$.
  (ii) Using the fact that $k = m$, solve the equation in (a)
    above to justify your stated value of x.

Solution

(a) Since the triangle is isosceles, angle KML = $x°$,
  angle LKM = $(180 - 2x)°$

Using the sine rule: $\dfrac{\sin L}{l} = \dfrac{\sin K}{k}$

$$\dfrac{\sin x°}{m} = \dfrac{\sin(180 - 2x)°}{k}$$

Since $\sin(180 - 2x)° = \sin 2x°$ $\dfrac{\sin x°}{m} = \dfrac{\sin 2x°}{k}$

(b) (i) When $k = m$, triangle KLM is equilateral, so $x = 60$

  (ii) $\dfrac{\sin x°}{m} = \dfrac{\sin 2x°}{k}$ becomes $\dfrac{\sin x°}{m} = \dfrac{\sin 2x°}{m}$

Hence $\sin x° = \sin 2x°$
$$\sin x° = 2\sin x° \cos x°$$
$$\sin x° - 2\sin x° \cos x° = 0$$
$$\sin x°(1 - 2\cos x°) = 0$$
$$\sin x° = 0 \text{ or } \cos x° = \tfrac{1}{2}$$
$$x = 0 \quad \text{or} \quad x = 60$$

Clearly $x = 60$ since the required angle is acute.

Revision exercise 11

U 1 Solve algebraically the following equations for $0 \leqslant x \leqslant 360$.
(a) $3\cos x° - 2 = 0$ (b) $\sin 3x° - 1 = 0$
(c) $2\sin^2 x° = 1$ (d) $3\sin(x + 30)° = 2$

U 2 Solve algebraically the following equations for $0 \leqslant x \leqslant 2\pi$.

(a) $\cos 2x = \dfrac{\sqrt{3}}{2}$ (b) $3\tan^2 x - 1 = 0$

(c) $\cos^2 x + \cos x = 0$ (d) $2 + 3\sin\left(2x - \dfrac{\pi}{6}\right) = 5$

U 3 In the diagrams below find the exact values of $\sin(p + q)$.
(a)

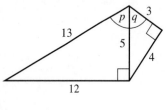

(b)

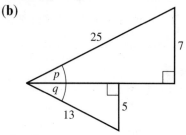

U 4 (a) Express $\sin x° \cos 60° - \cos x° \sin 60°$ in the form $\sin(A - B)°$.

(b) Hence solve the equation
$\sin x° \cos 60° - \cos x° \sin 60° = \frac{1}{2}$ for $0 \leqslant x \leqslant 180$.

U 5 (a) Express $\cos x \cos \dfrac{\pi}{4} + \sin x \sin \dfrac{\pi}{4}$ in the form $\cos(A - B)$.

(b) Hence solve the equation
$\cos x \cos \dfrac{\pi}{4} + \sin x \sin \dfrac{\pi}{4} = \dfrac{-1}{\sqrt{2}}$ for $0 \leqslant x \leqslant 2\pi$.

C 6 For acute angles P and Q, $\sin P = \dfrac{12}{13}$ and $\sin Q = \dfrac{3}{5}$.

Show that the exact value of $\sin(P + Q)$ is $\dfrac{63}{65}$.   [Higher]

C 7 Find the exact value of
(a) $\cos 75°$ (b) $\sin 105°$

C 8 Find the exact value of each of the following
(a) $\cos 25° \cos 20° - \sin 25° \sin 20°$
(b) $\cos 70° \cos 40° + \sin 70° \sin 40°$
(c) $\sin 70° \cos 10° - \cos 70° \sin 10°$
(d) $\cos 55° \sin 35° + \sin 55° \cos 35°$
(e) $2\sin 15° - 1$ (f) $\sin 75° \cos 75°$

C 9 Prove the following identities
(a) $(\sin x + \cos x)^2 = 1 + \sin 2x$
(b) $(\cos x + \sin x)(\cos x - \sin x) = \cos 2x$

(c) $\dfrac{(1 + \cos 2x)}{\sin 2x} = \dfrac{1}{\tan x}$

(d) $(\cos x + \sin x)^2 + (\cos x - \sin x)^2 = 2$

C 10 Show that $\cos\left(x - \dfrac{\pi}{6}\right) - \cos\left(x + \dfrac{\pi}{6}\right) = \sin x$

C 11 By expressing $3A$ as $(2A + A)$ prove that

(a) $\cos 3A = 4\cos^3 A - 3\cos A$

(b) $\sin 3A = 3\sin A - 4\sin^3 A$

C 12 Solve the following equations where $0 \leqslant x \leqslant 2\pi$.

(a) $\sin 2x - \sin x = 0$ (b) $\cos 2x - \sin x = 0$

(c) $\cos 2x = 2\sin^2 x$ (d) $\cos 2x - 4\cos x - 5 = 0$

C 13 The diagram shows two curves $y = \cos 2x$ and $y = 1 + \sin x$, where $0 \leqslant x \leqslant 360$.
Find the x-coordinate of the point of intersection at A.

[Higher]

C 14 Given that $\sin A = \dfrac{3}{4}$, where $0 \leqslant A \leqslant \dfrac{\pi}{2}$, find the **exact** value of $\sin 2A$.   [Higher]

C 15 Find, correct to one decimal place, the value of x, $180 \leqslant x \leqslant 270$, which satisfies the equation $3\cos(2x - 40)° - 1 = 0$.   [Higher]

C 16 In triangle PQR, prove that $p = 4q\cos x\cos 2x$.

C 17 In triangle ABC, prove that
$$c = \frac{b\sin(x + y)}{\sin y}$$

C 18 In isosceles triangle PQR, prove that
$$p = \frac{q\sin 2\alpha}{\cos\alpha}$$
Hence show that $p = 2q\sin\alpha$.

C 19 (a) Show that for the isosceles triangle opposite
$$\frac{q}{\sin x} = \frac{p}{\cos\dfrac{x}{2}}$$

(b) Hence, or otherwise, show that $q = 2p\sin\dfrac{x}{2}$

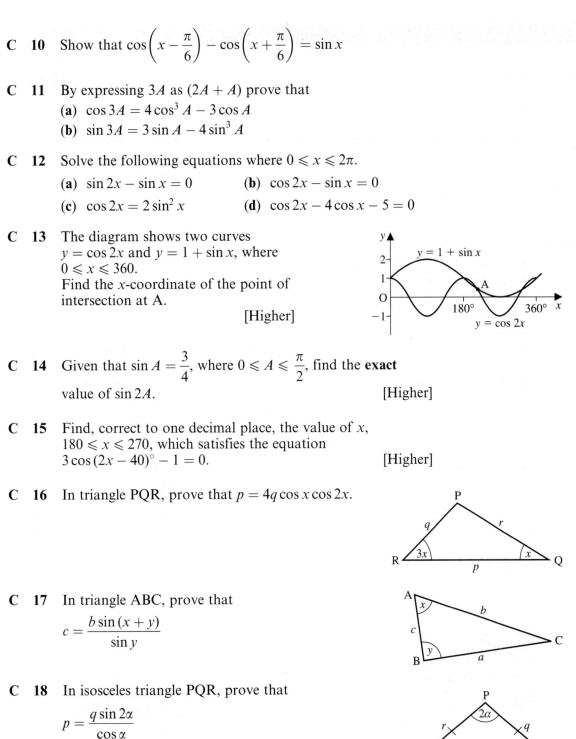

Test yourself	**What to review**

U 1 Solve algebraically the equation $2\sin 2x = -1$ for $0 \leqslant x \leqslant \pi$

Review Heinemann Higher Mathematics Chapter 4, pages 63 to 65

U 2 The diagram shows two right-angled triangles.

Review Heinemann Higher Mathematics Chapter 11, page 194

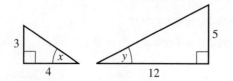

    (a) Write the values of $\cos x$ and $\sin y$.
    (b) By expanding $\cos(x - y)$ show that the exact
        value of $\cos(x - y)$ is $\dfrac{63}{65}$.

U 3 **(a)** Express $\sin x° \cos 60° - \cos x° \sin 60°$ in the form $\sin(A - B)$.
    (b) Hence solve the equation
        $\sin x° \cos 60° - \cos x° \sin 60° = \dfrac{3}{4}$ for $0 \leqslant x \leqslant 360$.

Review Heinemann Higher Mathematics Chapter 4, page 64 and Chapter 11, page 188

C 4 Solve algebraically for $0 \leqslant x \leqslant 360$
    $4\cos 2x - 2\sin x - 1 = 0$

Review Heinemann Higher Mathematics Chapter 11, page 198

C 5 In the diagram below $QR = RS = 1$. Use the expansion for $\sin(A + B)°$ to show that
$$\sqrt{3}\sin x° + \cos x° = \frac{4}{\sqrt{7}}$$

Review Heinemann Higher Mathematics Chapter 11, page 194

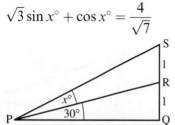

C 6 Prove that $\dfrac{\cos(x - y)}{\cos x \cos y} = 1 + \tan x \tan y$

Review Heinemann Higher Mathematics Chapter 11, page 192

Test yourself answers

1 $\dfrac{7\pi}{12}, \dfrac{11\pi}{12}$ **2** (a) $\dfrac{4}{5}, \dfrac{5}{13}$ **3** (a) $\sin(x - 60)°$ **(b)** $108.6°, 191.4°$ **4** $30°, 150°, 228.6°, 311.4°$

12 The circle

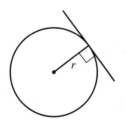
Outcome 4

Use the equation of the circle.

Performance criteria

PC(a)   Given the centre (a, b) and radius r, find the equation of the circle in the form $(x - a)^2 + (y - b)^2 = r^2$.

PC(b)   Find the radius and centre of a circle given the equation in the form $x^2 + y^2 + 2gx + 2fy + c = 0$.

PC(c)   Determine whether a given line is a tangent to a given circle.

PC(d)   Determine the equation of the tangent to a given circle given the point of contact.

U Example 1

Find the equation of a circle with centre C(5, −2) and passing through the point D(1, −5).

Solution

Length of radius = CD = $\sqrt{(x_2 - x_1)^2 + (y_2 - y_1)^2}$

$$= \sqrt{(1-5)^2 + (-5-(-2))^2}$$

$$= \sqrt{16+9}$$

$$= 5$$

Equation of circle is $(x-5)^2 + (y-(-2))^2 = 5^2$

$$(x-5)^2 + (y+2)^2 = 25$$

U Example 2

Find the radius and the centre of the circle with equation $x^2 + y^2 + 2x - 6y + 1 = 0$.

Solution

From the general equation of a circle $x^2 + y^2 + 2gx + 2fy + c = 0$

$2g = 2$ therefore $g = 1$

$2f = -6$ therefore $f = -3$

$$c = 1$$

The centre of the circle is $(-g, -f)$, that is $(-1, 3)$

The radius of the circle = $\sqrt{g^2 + f^2 - c}$

$$= \sqrt{1^2 + (-3)^2 - 1}$$

$$= \sqrt{9}$$

$$= 3$$

U Example 3

(a) Show that the straight line with equation $y = -3x + 6$ is a tangent to the circle with equation $x^2 + y^2 + 10x - 2y - 14 = 0$.

(b) Find the point of contact.

Solution

(a) Substitute $(-3x + 6)$ for y in the circle equation.

$x^2 + (-3x + 6)^2 + 10x - 2(-3x + 6) - 14 = 0$

$x^2 + 9x^2 - 36x + 36 + 10x + 6x - 12 - 14 = 0$

$10x^2 - 20x + 10 = 0$

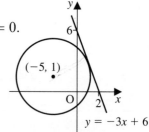

To examine the roots of this quadratic find the discriminant.

$b^2 - 4ac = (-20)^2 - 4 \times 10 \times 10$

$$= 400 - 400$$

$$= 0$$

Since the discriminant is zero the roots are equal. There is only one point of intersection. The line is a tangent to the circle.

(b) Solving the equation $10x^2 - 20x + 10 = 0$

$$10(x-1)(x-1) = 0$$

The quadratic has equal roots with $x = 1$

$$y = -3 \times 1 + 6$$

$$y = 3$$

The point of contact is (1, 3).

U Example 4

The point A(1, 8) lies on the circle with equation $x^2 + y^2 + 8x + 4y - 105 = 0$. Find the equation of the tangent at A.

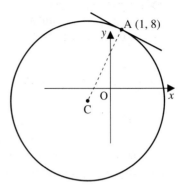

Solution

The centre of circle
$x^2 + y^2 + 8x + 4y - 105 = 0$ is C(-4, -2).

$$m_{CA} = \frac{8 - (-2)}{1 - (-4)} = \frac{10}{5} = 2$$

Since the tangent is perpendicular to the radius,
$m_{\tan} \times m_{\text{rad}} = -1$
So $m_{\tan} = -\frac{1}{2}$
Equation of tangent at A is $y - 8 = -\frac{1}{2}(x - 1)$
$$2y - 16 = -x + 1$$
$$x + 2y - 17 = 0$$

Revision exercise 12

U 1 Write the equation of the circle with centre the origin and radius
   (a) 8   **(b)** 13   **(c)** p

U 2 Find the equation of the circle which is concentric with $x^2 + y^2 = 7$ and has double the radius.

U 3 State the centre and radius of each circle.
   (a) $(x - 4)^2 + (y + 9)^2 = 49$ **(b)** $x^2 + (y + 11)^2 = 44$

U 4 Write the equation of the circle with the given centre and radius.
   (a) (2, 3), $r = 5$ **(b)** (-7, 1), $r = 3\sqrt{7}$ **(c)** (t, u), $r = a$

U 5 For each circle find the centre and the radius.
   (a) $x^2 + y^2 + 8x + 2y + 1 = 0$
   (b) $x^2 + y^2 - 12x + 8y - 12 = 0$
   (c) $x^2 + y^2 - 2x - 6y + 3 = 0$
   (d) $x^2 + y^2 - 14x = 0$

U 6 Find the equation of each circle with the given centre and radius.
Write your answer in the form $x^2 + y^2 + 2gx + 2fy + c = 0$.
   (a) (-1, 4), $r = 5$ **(b)** (3, -3), $r = 9$ **(c)** (2, 0), $r = 1$

U 7 Show that these lines are tangents to the given circles and find the points of contact.
   (a) $x^2 + y^2 = 18$
       $x + y = 6$
   (b) $x^2 + y^2 + 12x - 10y + 43 = 0$
       $y = x + 5$
   (c) $x^2 + y^2 - 12x + 8y + 26 = 0$
       $y = -5x$
   (d) $x^2 + y^2 - 16x + 4y + 23 = 0$
       $y - 2x + 3 = 0$

U **8** The point Q(3, 1) lies on the circle with the centre (−5, −3), as shown in the diagram. Find the equation of the tangent at Q.

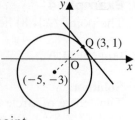

U **9** Find the equation of the tangent to each circle at the given point.
(a) $x^2 + y^2 = 45$ at the point A(6, 3).
(b) $x^2 + y^2 - 16x + 2y - 25 = 0$ at the point P(−1, 2).
(c) $x^2 + y^2 - 2x - 8y - 8 = 0$ at the point T(−3, 1).

C **10** The point (−5, 3) lies on the circumference of the circle $x^2 + y^2 + ax - 6y + 4 = 0$. Find the value of a.

C **11** The centre of the larger circle is A(6, 6).
The x-axis is a tangent to both circles.
The radii are in the ratio 2 : 1.
Find the equations of both circles.

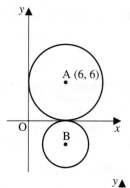

C **12** The equation of the circle with centre A is
$x^2 + y^2 - 14x - 12y + 60 = 0$.
The equation of the circle with centre D is
$x^2 + y^2 + 18x + 12y + 17 = 0$.
AD cuts the circumferences at B and C as shown.
Find the length of BC.

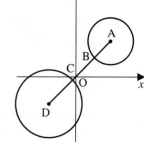

C **13** Find the equations of the tangents to
$x^2 + y^2 - 14x - 2y + 5 = 0$ which pass through Q(0, 2).

C **14** A penny-farthing bicycle on display in a museum is supported by a stand at points A and C.
A and C lie on the front wheel.
With coordinate axes as shown and 1 unit = 5 cm the equation of the rear wheel (the small wheel) is $x^2 + y^2 - 6y = 0$ and the equation of the front wheel is $x^2 + y^2 - 28x - 20y + 196 = 0$.
(a) (i) Find the distance between the centres of the two wheels.
(ii) Hence calculate the clearance, i.e. the smallest gap, between the front and rear wheels. Give your answer to the nearest millimetre.

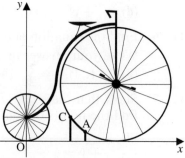

(b) B(7, 3) is half-way between A and C, and P is the centre of the front wheel.
(i) Find the gradient of PB.
(ii) Hence find the equation of AC and the coordinates of A and C. [Higher]

Test yourself	What to review
	If your answer is incorrect:

U 1 Write the equation of the circle with centre $(-5, 2)$ and radius $2\sqrt{5}$.

Review Heinemann Higher Mathematics Chapter 12, pages 209 to 211

U 2 State the centre and the radius of the circle $x^2 + y^2 + 8x - 14y + 1 = 0$.

Review Heinemann Higher Mathematics Chapter 12, pages 211 to 215

U 3 Show that the line $3x - y + 6 = 0$ is a tangent to the circle $x^2 + y^2 + 14x - 10y + 34 = 0$ and find the point of contact.

Review Heinemann Higher Mathematics Chapter 12, pages 217 to 219

U 4 The point R$(-2, 2)$ lies on the circle with the centre $(2, 5)$, as shown in the diagram. Find the equation of the tangent at R.

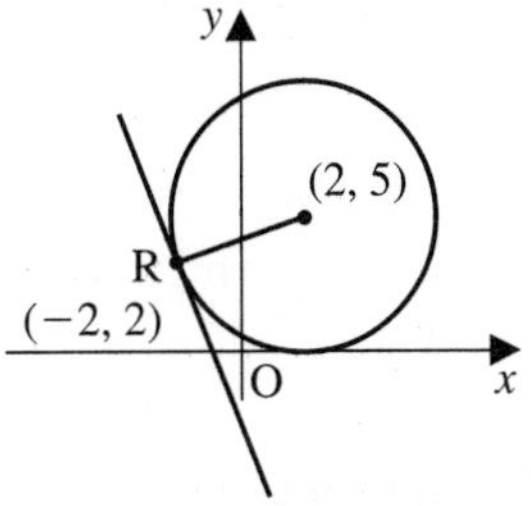

Review Heinemann Higher Mathematics Chapter 12, pages 219 and 220

U 5 Find the equation of the tangent to the circle $x^2 + y^2 - 16x + 12y + 87 = 0$ at the point $(6, -3)$.

Review Heinemann Higher Mathematics Chapter 12, pages 219 and 220

C 6 Find the centres and radii of the circles $x^2 + y^2 + 14x - 6y - 42 = 0$ and $x^2 + y^2 - 10x + 12y + 36 = 0$. Show that the circles touch externally.

Review Heinemann Higher Mathematics Chapter 12, pages 211 to 215

C 7 (a) Find the equation of the tangent to $x^2 + y^2 - 8x + 4y - 20 = 0$ at P$(-2, -4)$.
(b) Show that this line is also a tangent to $x^2 + y^2 = 10$ and find the point of contact Q.
(c) Calculate the length of the common tangent PQ.

Review Heinemann Higher Mathematics Chapter 12, pages 217 to 220

Test yourself answers

1 $(x + 5)^2 + (y - 2)^2 = 20$ **2** $(-4, 7), r = 8$ **3** $(-1, 3)$ **4** $4x + 3y = -2$ **5** $2x - 3y = 21$
6 $(-7, 3), r = 10$ and $(5, -6), r = 5$ **7** (a) $3x + y = -10$ (b) Q$(-3, -1)$ (c) PQ $= \sqrt{10}$

13 Vectors

Key points to remember

1 A **vector** is a quantity with both magnitude (size) and direction. A vector is named using either the letters at the end of the directed line segment $\overrightarrow{AB}$ or a bold letter **u**. A vector may also be represented by its **components**. These are known as **column vectors**.

$$\overrightarrow{AB} = \mathbf{u} = \begin{pmatrix} 4 \\ -3 \end{pmatrix}$$

2 If $\overrightarrow{PQ} = \begin{pmatrix} a \\ b \\ c \end{pmatrix}$ then $|\overrightarrow{PQ}| = \sqrt{a^2 + b^2 + c^2}$

3 If vector $\mathbf{v} = \begin{pmatrix} x \\ y \\ z \end{pmatrix}$ then $k\mathbf{v} = \begin{pmatrix} kx \\ ky \\ kz \end{pmatrix}$ and vector $k\mathbf{v}$ is parallel to vector $\mathbf{v}$.

Hence if $\mathbf{u} = k\mathbf{v}$ then $\mathbf{u}$ is parallel to $\mathbf{v}$.
Conversely if $\mathbf{u}$ is parallel to $\mathbf{v}$ then $\mathbf{u} = k\mathbf{v}$.

4 $\overrightarrow{OA}$ is called the **position vector** of the point A relative to origin O, written $\mathbf{a}$.
$\overrightarrow{OB}$ is called the position vector of B, written $\mathbf{b}$.
$\overrightarrow{AB} = \mathbf{b} - \mathbf{a}$ where $\mathbf{a}$ and $\mathbf{b}$ are the position vectors of A and B.

5 Points are said to be **collinear** if they lie on a straight line. If $\overrightarrow{AB} = k\overrightarrow{BC}$, where k is a scalar, then $\overrightarrow{AB}$ is parallel to $\overrightarrow{BC}$. If B is also a point common to both $\overrightarrow{AB}$ and $\overrightarrow{BC}$ then A, B and C are collinear.

6 A vector may also be defined in terms of **i**, **j** and **k**, where **i**, **j** and **k** are unit vectors in the x, y and z directions, respectively. In component form these vectors are written as

$$\mathbf{i} = \begin{pmatrix} 1 \\ 0 \\ 0 \end{pmatrix}, \mathbf{j} = \begin{pmatrix} 0 \\ 1 \\ 0 \end{pmatrix} \text{ and } \mathbf{k} = \begin{pmatrix} 0 \\ 0 \\ 1 \end{pmatrix}.$$

7 If $\mathbf{p}$ is the position vector of the point P that divides AB in the ratio $m:n$ then

$$\mathbf{p} = \frac{n}{m+n}\,\mathbf{a} + \frac{m}{m+n}\,\mathbf{b}$$

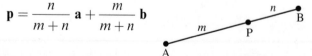

8 For two vectors $\mathbf{a}$ and $\mathbf{b}$ the scalar product is defined as $\mathbf{a}.\mathbf{b} = |\mathbf{a}\,||\,\mathbf{b}|\cos\theta$, where θ is the angle between $\mathbf{a}$ and $\mathbf{b}$, $0 \leqslant \theta \leqslant 180°$.

9 If $\mathbf{a} = \begin{pmatrix} a_1 \\ a_2 \\ a_3 \end{pmatrix}$ and $\mathbf{b} = \begin{pmatrix} b_1 \\ b_2 \\ b_3 \end{pmatrix}$ then $\mathbf{a}.\mathbf{b} = a_1 b_1 + a_2 b_2 + a_3 b_3$

10 If **a** and **b** are perpendicular then **a.b** $= 0$.
Conversely if **a.b** $= 0$ then **a** and **b** are perpendicular.

11 $\cos \theta = \dfrac{a_1 b_1 + a_2 b_2 + a_3 b_3}{|\mathbf{a}| \, |\mathbf{b}|}$ or $\cos \theta = \dfrac{\mathbf{a.b}}{|\mathbf{a}| \, |\mathbf{b}|}$

12 For vectors **a** and **b**, **a.b** $=$ **b.a**

13 For vectors **a**, **b** and **c**, **a.(b + c)** $=$ **a.b** $+$ **a.c**

Outcome 1

Use vectors in three dimensions.

Performance criteria

PC(a) Determine whether three points with given coordinates are collinear.
PC(b) Determine the coordinates of the point which divides the join of two given points internally in a given numerical ratio.
PC(c) Use the scalar product.

U Example 1

For the points P(-2, 1, 5) and Q(-3, -5, 6) find the components of $\overrightarrow{PQ}$ and calculate its magnitude.

Solution

$\overrightarrow{PQ} = \mathbf{q} - \mathbf{p}$

$$= \begin{pmatrix} -3 \\ -5 \\ 6 \end{pmatrix} - \begin{pmatrix} -2 \\ 1 \\ 5 \end{pmatrix}$$

$$= \begin{pmatrix} -1 \\ -6 \\ 1 \end{pmatrix}$$

$|\overrightarrow{PQ}| = \sqrt{(-1)^2 + (-6)^2 + 1^2}$

$\qquad = \sqrt{38}$

U Example 2

A, B and C have coordinates (2, 4, 6), (6, 6, 2) and (14, 10, -6).

(a) Write down the components of $\overrightarrow{AB}$.
(b) Hence show that A, B and C are collinear.
(c) Find the value of AB : BC.

Solution

(a) $\overrightarrow{AB} = \mathbf{b} - \mathbf{a} = \begin{pmatrix} 6 \\ 6 \\ 2 \end{pmatrix} - \begin{pmatrix} 2 \\ 4 \\ 6 \end{pmatrix} = \begin{pmatrix} 4 \\ 2 \\ -4 \end{pmatrix}$

(b) $\overrightarrow{BC} = c - b = \begin{pmatrix} 14 \\ 10 \\ -6 \end{pmatrix} - \begin{pmatrix} 6 \\ 6 \\ 2 \end{pmatrix} = \begin{pmatrix} 8 \\ 4 \\ -8 \end{pmatrix}$

$\overrightarrow{BC} = 2\overrightarrow{AB}$ hence $\overrightarrow{BC}$ is parallel to $\overrightarrow{AB}$. Since B is a point in common, A, B and C are collinear.

(c) AB:BC = 1:2

U **Example 3**

P divides AB in the ratio 3:2. If A is the point $(-3, 1, 1)$ and B is $(2, 1, -4)$, find the coordinates of P.

Solution

$p = \dfrac{2a}{5} + \dfrac{3b}{5}$

$= \dfrac{1}{5}(2a + 3b)$

$= \dfrac{1}{5}\left[2\begin{pmatrix} -3 \\ 1 \\ 1 \end{pmatrix} + 3\begin{pmatrix} 2 \\ 1 \\ -4 \end{pmatrix} \right]$

$= \dfrac{1}{5}\begin{pmatrix} 0 \\ 5 \\ -10 \end{pmatrix} = \begin{pmatrix} 0 \\ 1 \\ -2 \end{pmatrix}$

P has coordinates $(0, 1, -2)$.

U **Example 4**

Points P, Q and R have coordinates $(-1, 0, 3)$, $(2, 3, -1)$ and $(1, 5, -4)$.

(a) Calculate $\overrightarrow{QP}.\overrightarrow{QR}$

(b) Hence find the size of angle PQR.

Solution

(a) $\overrightarrow{QP} = \quad p \quad - \quad q \qquad\qquad \overrightarrow{QR} = \quad r \quad - \quad q$

$\qquad = \begin{pmatrix} -1 \\ 0 \\ 3 \end{pmatrix} - \begin{pmatrix} 2 \\ 3 \\ -1 \end{pmatrix} \qquad\qquad = \begin{pmatrix} 1 \\ 5 \\ -4 \end{pmatrix} - \begin{pmatrix} 2 \\ 3 \\ -1 \end{pmatrix}$

$\qquad = \begin{pmatrix} -3 \\ -3 \\ 4 \end{pmatrix} \qquad\qquad\qquad = \begin{pmatrix} -1 \\ 2 \\ -3 \end{pmatrix}$

Hence $\overrightarrow{QP}.\overrightarrow{QR} = -3.-1 + -3.2 + 4.-3$

$\qquad\qquad\qquad = -15$

(b) $\cos PQR = \dfrac{\overrightarrow{QP}.\overrightarrow{QR}}{|\overrightarrow{QP}\| \overrightarrow{QR}|} = \dfrac{-15}{\sqrt{(-3)^2+(-3)^2+4^2} \times \sqrt{(-1)^2+2^2+(-3)^2}}$

$$= \dfrac{-15}{\sqrt{34} \times \sqrt{14}}$$

$$\cos PQR = -0.688$$

Hence angle PQR is 133.4°.

U Example 5

For vectors $\mathbf{a} = \begin{pmatrix} 2 \\ -1 \\ -3 \end{pmatrix}$ and $\mathbf{b} = \begin{pmatrix} -1 \\ 1 \\ p \end{pmatrix}$ find p if $\mathbf{a}$ is

perpendicular to $\mathbf{b}$.

Solution

If $\mathbf{a}$ is perpendicular to $\mathbf{b}$ then $\mathbf{a}.\mathbf{b} = 0$

Hence, $2.-1 + -1.1 + -3.p = 0$

$$-3 - 3p = 0$$

$$p = -1$$

C Example 6

EFGH is a quadrilateral with vertices E(8, −2, 6), F(16, 6, −2),
G(0, 8, 8) and H(−8, 0, 16).
(a) Find the coordinates of M, the mid-point of EF.
(b) Find the coordinates of N, which divides GM in the ratio 2:1
(c) Find the ratio in which N divides FH.

Solution

(a) $\mathbf{m} = \dfrac{1}{2}(\mathbf{e} + \mathbf{f})$

$$= \dfrac{1}{2}\begin{pmatrix} 24 \\ 4 \\ 4 \end{pmatrix} = \begin{pmatrix} 12 \\ 2 \\ 2 \end{pmatrix}$$

M(12, 2, 2)

(b) $\mathbf{n} = \dfrac{2}{3}\mathbf{m} + \dfrac{1}{3}\mathbf{g}$

$$= \dfrac{1}{3}(2\mathbf{m} + \mathbf{g})$$

$$= \dfrac{1}{3}\left[\begin{pmatrix} 24 \\ 4 \\ 4 \end{pmatrix} + \begin{pmatrix} 0 \\ 8 \\ 8 \end{pmatrix}\right]$$

$$= \dfrac{1}{3}\begin{pmatrix} 24 \\ 12 \\ 12 \end{pmatrix} = \begin{pmatrix} 8 \\ 4 \\ 4 \end{pmatrix}$$

N(8, 4, 4)

(c) $\overrightarrow{FN} = \mathbf{n} - \mathbf{f}$

$= \begin{pmatrix} 8 \\ 4 \\ 4 \end{pmatrix} - \begin{pmatrix} 16 \\ 6 \\ -2 \end{pmatrix}$

$= \begin{pmatrix} -8 \\ -2 \\ 6 \end{pmatrix}$

$\overrightarrow{NH} = \mathbf{h} - \mathbf{n}$

$= \begin{pmatrix} -8 \\ 0 \\ 16 \end{pmatrix} - \begin{pmatrix} 8 \\ 4 \\ 4 \end{pmatrix}$

$= \begin{pmatrix} -16 \\ -4 \\ 12 \end{pmatrix}$

$\overrightarrow{NH} = 2\overrightarrow{FN}$, hence N divides $\overrightarrow{FH}$ in the ratio $1:2$.

C Example 7

The diagram shows a square-based pyramid. All edges are 2 units in length. Calculate $\mathbf{a}.(\mathbf{b} + \mathbf{c})$.

Solution

$\mathbf{a}.(\mathbf{b} + \mathbf{c}) = \mathbf{a}.\mathbf{b} + \mathbf{a}.\mathbf{c}$

$\qquad = 2 \times 2 \times \cos 60° + 2 \times 2 \times \cos 90°$

$\qquad = \qquad 2 \qquad + \qquad 0$

$\qquad = 2$

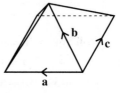

Revision exercise 13

U 1 A is the point $(4, -5)$ and B is $(-2, 1)$.

(a) Write down the components of $\overrightarrow{AB}$ and calculate $|\overrightarrow{AB}|$.

(b) Find the coordinates of M, the mid-point of AB.

(c) Find the coordinates of N, which divides AB in the ratio $2:1$.

U 2 P, Q and R have coordinates $(2, -4, 5)$, $(3, 1, 3)$ and $(6, 16, -3)$.

(a) Write down the components of $\overrightarrow{PQ}$.

(b) Hence show that the points P, Q and R are collinear.

[Higher]

U 3 Show that the points $A(3, -2, 0)$, $B(2, 1, 5)$ and $C(0, 7, 15)$ are collinear.

U 4 The point S divides XY in the ratio $3:2$. Find the coordinates of S.

$Y(-3, 4, 15)$

S

$X(2, -1, 5)$

U 5 For points $P(-6, -6, -6)$ and $R(3, 0, -3)$,

T divides $\overrightarrow{PR}$ in the ratio $2:1$. Find the coordinates of T.

R

T

P

U 6 In triangle ABC, $\overrightarrow{AB} = \begin{pmatrix} 3 \\ -1 \\ 4 \end{pmatrix}$ and $\overrightarrow{AC} = \begin{pmatrix} -1 \\ 2 \\ -1 \end{pmatrix}$

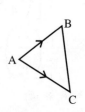

(a) Find the value of $\overrightarrow{AB}.\overrightarrow{AC}$

(b) Use the result of (a) to find the size of angle BAC.

U 7 In triangle FGH, F has coordinates (2, 3, 1), G is (5, −2, 3) and H is (−1, 0, 3). Calculate angle GFH.

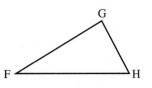

C 8 VABCD is a pyramid with rectangular base ABCD. The vectors $\overrightarrow{AB}$, $\overrightarrow{AD}$ and $\overrightarrow{AV}$ are given by

$$\overrightarrow{AB} = 8\mathbf{i} + 2\mathbf{j} + 2\mathbf{k}$$
$$\overrightarrow{AD} = -2\mathbf{i} + 10\mathbf{j} - 2\mathbf{k} \text{ and}$$
$$\overrightarrow{AV} = \mathbf{i} + 7\mathbf{j} + 7\mathbf{k}.$$

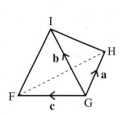

Express $\overrightarrow{CV}$ in component form.　　　　[Higher]

C 9 The diagram shows a regular tetrahedron of side 3 units. $\overrightarrow{GH} = \mathbf{a}$, $\overrightarrow{GI} = \mathbf{b}$ and $\overrightarrow{GF} = \mathbf{c}$.
(a) State the size of angle IGF.
(b) Evaluate (i) **b.c**
　　　　　(ii) **b.(c + a)**

C 10 A is the point (3, −2, 5), B is (2, 1, −3) and P is (1, 0, −7). Find Q such that $\overrightarrow{PQ}$ is parallel to $\overrightarrow{AB}$ and twice the magnitude.

C 11 Calculate the angle between the vectors **u** and **v** where $\mathbf{u} = 2\mathbf{i} + \mathbf{j} - 3\mathbf{k}$ and $\mathbf{v} = 5\mathbf{i} - \mathbf{k}$.

C 12 Prove that triangle XYZ is right-angled at Y.

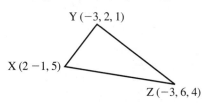

C 13 (a) A, B, C and D are the points (1, 2, 3), (7, −1, 5), (5, −7, 2) and (−1, −4, 0) respectively.
　　(i) Prove that AD = BC.
　　(ii) Prove that AC is perpendicular to BD.
　　(iii) Prove that AC = BD.
　　(iv) What kind of figure is ABCD?
　(b)

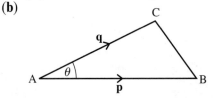

　　In the diagram **p** and **q** are unit vectors represented by $\overrightarrow{AB}$ and $\overrightarrow{AC}$ respectively. Angle BAC = θ.
　　If **p.q** = k, express the area of triangle ABC in terms of k and θ.　　　　[Higher]

C 14 A construction toy consists of rods and joints. Three joints L, M and N are placed around joint X as shown.

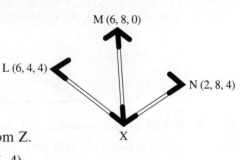

(a) Show that the cosine of angle MLN is 0.5
(b) Find the coordinates of Y, the mid-point of $\overrightarrow{LN}$.
(c) Find the coordinates of Z, which divides $\overrightarrow{MY}$ in the ratio 2:1.
(d) Show that L, M and N are equidistant from Z.

C 15 ABCD is a quadrilateral with vertices A(5, −6, 4), B(−4, 6, 7), C(−5, 10, −2) and D(4, −2, −5).

(a) Find the components of $\overrightarrow{AB}$ and then prove that ABCD is a parallelogram.
(b) If the point P divides $\overrightarrow{AB}$ internally in the ratio 2:1, calculate the coordinates of P.
(c) Show that PC is perpendicular to BD. [Higher]

C 16 A, B and C are the points (0, 5, 5), (4, 1, 1) and $(2\frac{1}{2}, 2\frac{1}{2}, 2\frac{1}{2})$ respectively.

(a) Prove that A, B and C are collinear and find the ratio in which C divides AB.
(b) O is the origin. Prove that $\overrightarrow{OC}$ bisects angle AOB.
(c) Given that **p**, **q** and **r** are position vectors of P, Q and R relative to the origin O and that $\overrightarrow{OQ}$ bisects angle POR, prove that $\dfrac{\mathbf{p.q}}{\mathbf{r.q}} = \dfrac{|\mathbf{p}|}{|\mathbf{r}|}$ [Higher]

C 17 LMNPQRST is a cuboid. X lies one-third of the way along $\overrightarrow{ST}$, (i.e. SX:XT = 1:2). Y lies one-quarter of the way along $\overrightarrow{QR}$, (i.e. QY:YR = 1:3). $\overrightarrow{LM}$, $\overrightarrow{LP}$ and $\overrightarrow{LQ}$ can be represented by the vectors $\begin{pmatrix} -12 \\ 0 \\ 6 \end{pmatrix}$, $\begin{pmatrix} -4 \\ 8 \\ -8 \end{pmatrix}$ and $\begin{pmatrix} 4 \\ 10 \\ 8 \end{pmatrix}$ respectively.

(a) Calculate the components of $\overrightarrow{LX}$.
(b) Calculate the components of $\overrightarrow{LY}$.
(c) Calculate the size of angle XLY.

C 18 The diagram shows two vectors **p** and **q**, with $|\mathbf{p}| = 2$ and $|\mathbf{q}| = 3$. The angle between the vectors is 60°.

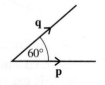

(a) Evaluate (i) **p.p**
(ii) **q.q**
(iii) **p.q**
(b) Another vector **v** is defined by $\mathbf{v} = 3\mathbf{p} + 2\mathbf{q}$. Evaluate **v.v** and hence write down $|\mathbf{v}|$.

Test yourself	**What to review**
	If your answer is incorrect:

U 1 A, B and C have coordinates (1, −3, 4), (−2, 1, 1) and (−11, 13, −8).

(a) Write down the components of $\overrightarrow{AC}$.

(b) Hence show that the points A, B and C are collinear.

Review Heinemann Higher Mathematics Chapter 13, pages 238 to 240

U 2 The point Q divides $\overrightarrow{PR}$ in the ratio 1:3. Find the coordinates of Q.

Review Heinemann Higher Mathematics Chapter 13, pages 241 and 242

U 3 The diagram shows triangle FGH where

$$\overrightarrow{FG} = \begin{pmatrix} 3 \\ 2 \\ -1 \end{pmatrix} \text{ and } \overrightarrow{FH} = \begin{pmatrix} 2 \\ -1 \\ 0 \end{pmatrix}$$

Review Heinemann Higher Mathematics Chapter 13, pages 251 to 253

(a) Find the value of $\overrightarrow{FG}.\overrightarrow{FH}$.

(b) Use the result of (a) to find the size of angle GFH.

C 4 Vector $a\mathbf{i} + b\mathbf{j} - \mathbf{k}$ is perpendicular to both $3\mathbf{i} + \mathbf{j} + 11\mathbf{k}$ and $-2\mathbf{i} - \mathbf{j} - 9\mathbf{k}$. Find the values of a and b.

Review Heinemann Higher Mathematics Chapter 13, page 254

C 5 EFGHIJKL is a cuboid. A lies two-thirds of the way along $\overrightarrow{KL}$. B lies one-quarter of the way along $\overrightarrow{IJ}$. $\overrightarrow{EF}$, $\overrightarrow{EH}$ and $\overrightarrow{EI}$ can be represented by the vectors

$$\begin{pmatrix} 6 \\ -12 \\ 0 \end{pmatrix}, \begin{pmatrix} 4 \\ 2 \\ -4 \end{pmatrix} \text{ and } \begin{pmatrix} 4 \\ 2 \\ 5 \end{pmatrix} \text{ respectively.}$$

Review Heinemann Higher Mathematics Chapter 13, pages 233, 234, 239 and 253

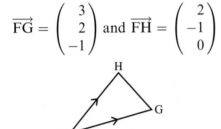

(a) Calculate the components of $\overrightarrow{EB}$.

(b) Calculate the components of $\overrightarrow{EA}$.

(c) Calculate the size of angle AEB.

C   6   The diagram shows two vectors **r** and **s**, with $|\mathbf{r}| = 4$ and $|\mathbf{s}| = \sqrt{3}$.
The angle between **r** and **s** is 30°.

Review Heinemann Higher Mathematics Chapter 13, pages 250 to 253

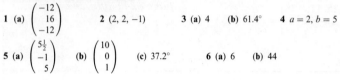

(a) Evaluate **r.s**

(b) If $\mathbf{p} = 2\mathbf{r}$ and $\mathbf{q} = \mathbf{r} + \mathbf{s}$, evaluate **p.q**.

Test yourself answers

1 (a) $\begin{pmatrix} -12 \\ 16 \\ -12 \end{pmatrix}$ **2** $(2, 2, -1)$ **3** (a) 4   (b) 61.4°   **4** $a = 2, b = 5$

5 (a) $\begin{pmatrix} 5\frac{1}{2} \\ -1 \\ 5 \end{pmatrix}$ (b) $\begin{pmatrix} 10 \\ 0 \\ 1 \end{pmatrix}$ (c) 37.2°   **6** (a) 6   (b) 44

14 Further calculus

Key points to remember

1 $\frac{\mathrm{d}}{\mathrm{d}x}(\sin x) = \cos x \qquad \frac{\mathrm{d}}{\mathrm{d}x}(\cos x) = -\sin x$

2 $\int \cos x \,\mathrm{d}x = \sin x + C \qquad \int \sin x \,\mathrm{d}x = -\cos x + C$

3 The **chain rule**:

If $\mathrm{h}(x) = \mathrm{f}(\mathrm{g}(x))$ then $\mathrm{h}'(x) = \mathrm{f}'(\mathrm{g}(x)).\mathrm{g}'(x)$ or $\frac{\mathrm{d}y}{\mathrm{d}x} = \frac{\mathrm{d}y}{\mathrm{d}u} \times \frac{\mathrm{d}u}{\mathrm{d}x}$

4 $\int (ax+b)^n \,\mathrm{d}x = \frac{(ax+b)^{n+1}}{a(n+1)} + C$

5 $\int \cos(ax+b)\,\mathrm{d}x = \frac{1}{a}\sin(ax+b) + C$

$\int \sin(ax+b)\,\mathrm{d}x = -\frac{1}{a}\cos(ax+b) + C$

Outcome 2

Use further differentiation and integration.

Performance criteria

PC(a) Differentiate $k\sin x$, $k\cos x$.

PC(b) Differentiate using the function of a function rule.

PC(c) Integrate functions of the form $\mathrm{f}(x) = (x+q)^n$, n rational except for -1, $\mathrm{f}(x) = p\cos x$ and $\mathrm{f}(x) = p\sin x$.

U Example 1

Differentiate $2\cos x + \frac{2}{3}\sin x$ with respect to x.

Solution

$$\mathrm{f}(x) = 2\cos x + \tfrac{2}{3}\sin x$$

$$\mathrm{f}'(x) = 2(-\sin x) + \tfrac{2}{3}\cos x$$

$$= -2\sin x + \tfrac{2}{3}\cos x$$

U Example 2

Given that $\mathrm{f}(x) = (x^2+3)^8$ find $\mathrm{f}'(x)$.

Solution

$$\mathrm{f}(x) = (x^2+3)^8$$

$$\mathrm{f}'(x) = 8(x^2+3)^7 \times 2x$$

$$= 16x(x^2+3)^7$$

U Example 3

Find $\int 3\sin x - \frac{1}{2}\cos x\,dx$.

Solution

$$\int 3\sin x - \frac{1}{2}\cos x\,dx = 3\times(-\cos x) - \frac{1}{2}\sin x + C$$
$$= -3\cos x - \frac{1}{2}\sin x + C$$

C Example 4

Evaluate $\int_1^2 (2x+1)^3\,dx$.

Solution

$$\int_1^2 (2x+1)^3\,dx = \left[\frac{(2x+1)^4}{4\times 2}\right]_1^2$$
$$= \left[\frac{1}{8}(2x+1)^4\right]_1^2$$
$$= \frac{1}{8}((2\times 2+1)^4 - (2\times 1+1)^4)$$
$$= \frac{1}{8}(625 - 81)$$
$$= 68$$

C Example 5

The diagram shows the graphs of $y = -\sin x$
and $y = \cos x$.
(a) Find the coordinates of A.
(b) Hence find the shaded area.

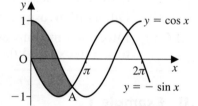

Solution

(a) Solve simultaneously $y = -\sin x$ and $y = \cos x$

$$-\sin x = \cos x$$

$$\frac{-\sin x}{\cos x} = 1$$

$$\tan x = -1$$

$$x = \frac{5\pi}{4} \quad\text{or}\quad \frac{7\pi}{4}$$

when $x = \dfrac{5\pi}{4}$, $y = \dfrac{-1}{\sqrt{2}}$

The coordinates of A are $\left(\dfrac{5\pi}{4}, \dfrac{-1}{\sqrt{2}}\right)$

(b) Shaded area $= \displaystyle\int_0^{\frac{5\pi}{4}} \cos x - (-\sin x)\,dx$

$$= \int_0^{\frac{5\pi}{4}} \cos x + \sin x\,dx$$

$$= \Big[\sin x - \cos x\Big]_0^{\frac{5\pi}{4}}$$

$$= \left(\sin\frac{5\pi}{4} - \cos\frac{5\pi}{4}\right) - (\sin 0 - \cos 0)$$

$$= \left(-\frac{1}{\sqrt{2}} - \left(-\frac{1}{\sqrt{2}}\right)\right) - (-1)$$

$$= 1$$

C Example 6

Find $\displaystyle\int \sin 2x - \cos\left(3x - \frac{\pi}{4}\right)\,dx$.

Solution

$$\int \sin 2x - \cos\left(3x - \frac{\pi}{4}\right)\,dx = -\frac{1}{2}\cos 2x - \frac{1}{3}\sin\left(3x - \frac{\pi}{4}\right) + C$$

Revision exercise 14

U 1 Differentiate the following with respect to x.
    (a) $5\sin x$ (b) $-3\cos x$

    (c) $\frac{2}{3}\cos x - 2\sin x$ (d) $3\cos x - \frac{2}{5}\sin x$

    (e) $\dfrac{\cos x}{2}$ (f) $\dfrac{-\sin x}{5}$

U 2 Find
    (a) $\displaystyle\int 3\cos x\,dx$ (b) $\displaystyle\int -2\sin\theta\,d\theta$ (c) $\displaystyle\int \frac{2}{7}\sin t\,dt$

U 3 Find $\dfrac{dy}{dx}$ for each of the following.
    (a) $y = (x^2 - 3)^4$ (b) $y = (3x^3 - 2x^2 + 1)^5$
    (c) $y = (x - 2)^{10}$ (d) $y = \sin 4x$
    (e) $y = \cos 4x - 3\sin 2x$ (f) $y = -\sin(3 - 2x)$

    (g) $y = \dfrac{5}{(x^2 + 3)^4}$ (h) $y = \sqrt{(5 - 3x^4)}$

    (i) $y = \cos^4 x$ (j) $y = \sqrt{(\sin x)}$

    (k) $y = \sin^2 x$ (l) $y = \dfrac{1}{\sqrt{(2x - 1)}}$

U 4   Find

$$\text{(a)} \int_0^1 (2x + 3)^6 \, dx \qquad \text{(b)} \int_{-1}^1 (5 - t)^3 \, dt \qquad \text{(c)} \int_0^{\frac{\pi}{3}} 3 \sin \theta \, d\theta$$

C 5   For each curve find the equation of the tangent at the given point.

(a) $y = (2x - 1)^4$ when $x = 2$ (b) $y = \sin 2\theta$ when $\theta = \dfrac{\pi}{2}$

C 6   For each of the following curves find the stationary points and determine their nature.

(a) $y = (x^2 - 4)^3$ (b) $y = \sin^2 x$ for $0 \leqslant x \leqslant 2\pi$

C 7   Find $f'(1)$ if $f(x) = (x^2 + x + 1)^2$.

C 8   Calculate the shaded area in each diagram.

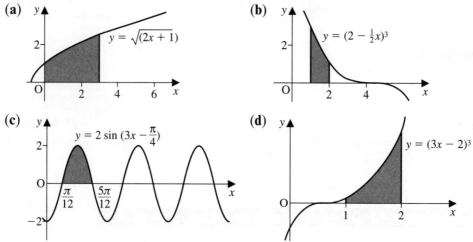

C 9   Find the shaded area between the curves in each diagram.

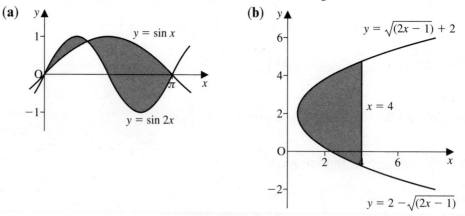

C 10   Find $f(x)$ if $f'(x) = (5x - 3)^5$ and $f(1) = 32$.

C 11   In a small factory the production cost, C, in pounds, of assembling x components in a month is given by

$$C(x) = \left(40x + \frac{2400}{x}\right)^2, \ x \neq 0. \text{ Calculate the minimum cost}$$

of production in any month and the corresponding number of components that are required to be built.

Test yourself	What to review
	If your answer is incorrect:
U 1 Differentiate the following with respect to x. **(a)** $5\cos x$ **(b)** $\frac{1}{4}\sin x$	*Review Heinemann Higher Mathematics Chapter 14, pages 263 and 264*
U 2 Differentiate the following with respect to x. **(a)** $(x^4 - 2)^5$ **(b)** $\sqrt{(1 - 2x)}$	*Review Heinemann Higher Mathematics Chapter 14, pages 269 and 270*
U 3 Find the following integrals. **(a)** $(3x - 2)^3$ **(b)** $\sqrt{(5x - 1)}$	*Review Heinemann Higher Mathematics Chapter 14, pages 273 and 274*
U 4 Find the following integrals. **(a)** $4\sin x$ **(b)** $\frac{1}{3}\cos x$	*Review Heinemann Higher Mathematics Chapter 14, page 275*
C 5 Find $f'(2)$ if $f(x) = \dfrac{1}{\sqrt{(2x^3 - 4)}}$.	*Review Heinemann Higher Mathematics Chapter 14, page 271*
C 6 Find the equation of the tangent to the curve $y = (2x - 10)^3$ at the point $(6, 8)$.	*Review Heinemann Higher Mathematics Chapter 14, page 271*
C 7 Find the shaded areas in each of the following diagrams.	*Review Heinemann Higher Mathematics Chapter 14, pages 273 and 275*

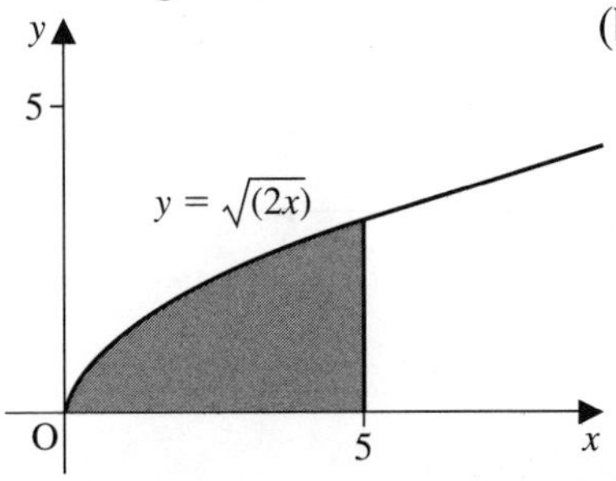

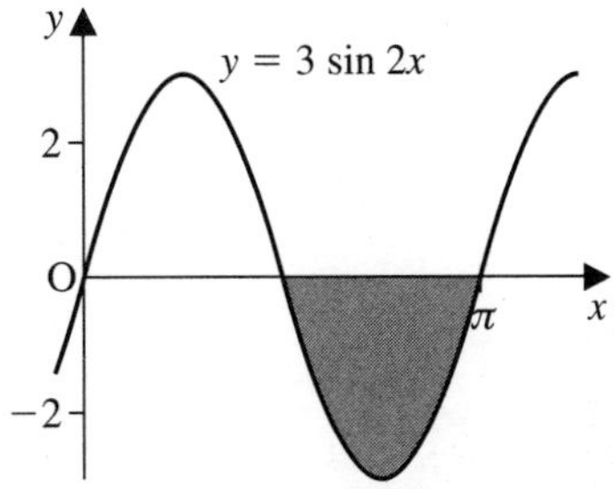

(a)

(b)

C 8 Find the area between the curves $y = \frac{1}{2}(x - 1)^3 + 1$ and $y = 2x - 1$.

Review Heinemann Higher Mathematics Chapter 14, pages 273 and 274

C 9 Find an expression for y if $\dfrac{dy}{dx} = \sin 2x$ and $y = 0$ when $x = \dfrac{\pi}{4}$.

Review Heinemann Higher Mathematics Chapter 14, page 275

Test yourself answers

1 (a) $-5\sin x$ **(b)** $\frac{1}{4}\cos x$ **2 (a)** $20x^3(x^4 - 2)^4$ **(b)** $\dfrac{-1}{\sqrt{(1 - 2x)}}$ **3 (a)** $\frac{1}{12}(3x - 2)^4 + C$ **(b)** $\frac{2}{15}(5x - 1)^{\frac{3}{2}} + C$ **4 (a)** $-4\cos x + C$

(b) $\frac{1}{3}\sin x + C$ **5** $\dfrac{-\sqrt{3}}{6}$ **6** $y = 24x - 136$ **7 (a)** $\dfrac{10\sqrt{10}}{3}$ square units **(b)** 3 square units   **8** 4 square units   **9** $y = -\frac{1}{2}\cos 2x$

15 Exponential and logarithmic functions

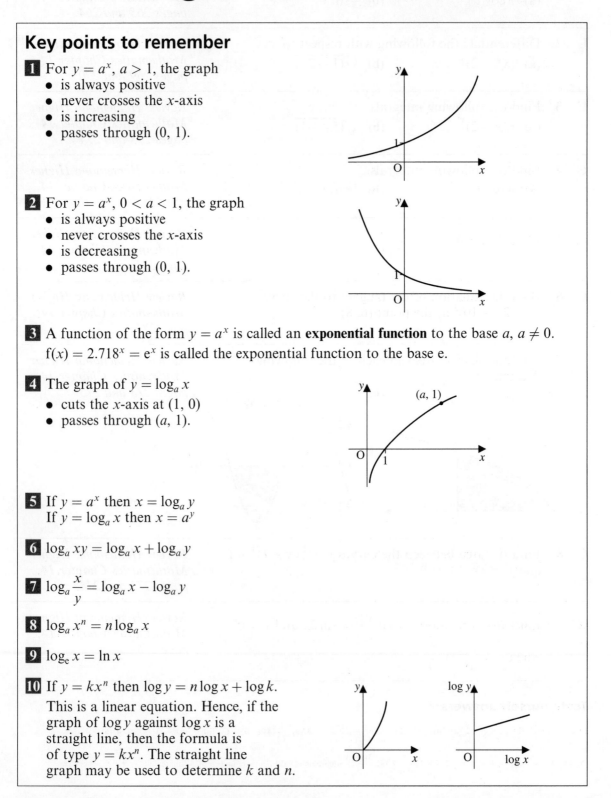

Key points to remember

1 For $y = a^x$, $a > 1$, the graph
- is always positive
- never crosses the x-axis
- is increasing
- passes through $(0, 1)$.

2 For $y = a^x$, $0 < a < 1$, the graph
- is always positive
- never crosses the x-axis
- is decreasing
- passes through $(0, 1)$.

3 A function of the form $y = a^x$ is called an **exponential function** to the base a, $a \neq 0$.
$f(x) = 2.718^x = e^x$ is called the exponential function to the base e.

4 The graph of $y = \log_a x$
- cuts the x-axis at $(1, 0)$
- passes through $(a, 1)$.

5 If $y = a^x$ then $x = \log_a y$
If $y = \log_a x$ then $x = a^y$

6 $\log_a xy = \log_a x + \log_a y$

7 $\log_a \dfrac{x}{y} = \log_a x - \log_a y$

8 $\log_a x^n = n \log_a x$

9 $\log_e x = \ln x$

10 If $y = kx^n$ then $\log y = n \log x + \log k$.
This is a linear equation. Hence, if the graph of $\log y$ against $\log x$ is a straight line, then the formula is of type $y = kx^n$. The straight line graph may be used to determine k and n.

11 If $y = ab^x$ then $\log y = \log a + x \log b$.
This is a linear equation. Hence, if the graph of $\log y$ against x is a straight line, then the formula is of type $y = ab^x$. The straight line graph may be used to determine a and b.

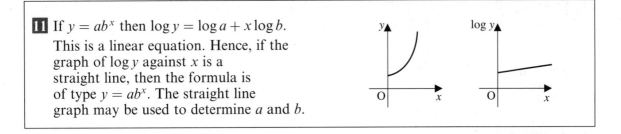

Outcome 3

Use properties of logarithmic and exponential functions.

Performance criteria
PC(a)   Simplify a numerical expression using the laws of logarithms.
PC(b)   Solve simple logarithmic and exponential equations.

U Example 1
Simplify
(a) $\log_4 64$
(b) $\log_4 16 + \log_4 8 - \log_4 32$
(c) $\frac{1}{3} \log_9 27$

Solution
(a) Since $\qquad 4^3 = 64$
$$\log_4 64 = \log_4 4^3 = 3$$

(b) $\log_4 16 + \log_4 8 - \log_4 32 = \log_4 \left(\dfrac{16 \times 8}{32} \right)$
$$= \log_4 4$$
$$= 1$$

(c) $\frac{1}{3} \log_9 27 = \log_9 \left(27^{\frac{1}{3}} \right)$
$$= \log_9 3$$
$$= \log_9 9^{\frac{1}{2}}$$
$$= \tfrac{1}{2}$$

U Example 2
Given $3^x = 10$, find an expression for the exact value of x.

Solution
$$3^x = 10$$
$$\log_{10} (3^x) = \log_{10} 10$$
$$x \log_{10} 3 = 1$$
$$x = \frac{1}{\log_{10} 3}$$

U   Example 3

Given that $\log_{10} y = 3.4$, write down an expression for the exact value of y.

Solution

$y = 10^{3.4}$

U   Example 4

Solve, for $x > 0$, $\log_7 (x^2 - 1) - \log_7 (x - 1) = 2$.

Solution

$$\log_7 (x^2 - 1) - \log_7 (x - 1) = 2$$

$$\log_7 \frac{(x^2 - 1)}{(x - 1)} = \log_7 49$$

$$\frac{x^2 - 1}{x - 1} = 49$$

notice that
$\log_7 49 = \log_7 7^2 = 2$

$$\frac{(x + 1)(x - 1)}{x - 1} = 49$$

$$x + 1 = 49$$

$$x = 48$$

C   Example 5

The air pressure in a life raft falls according to the formula $P_t = P_0 e^{-kt}$, where P_0 is the initial pressure, P_t is the pressure at time t hours and k is a constant.

(a) At time zero the pressure is 80 units. 12 hours later it is 60 units. Find the value of k to two significant figures.

(b) When the pressure is below 40 units the raft is unsafe. From time zero, for how long is the raft safe to use?

Solution

(a) $P_t = P_0 e^{-kt}$

$$60 = 80 e^{-k(12)}$$

$$e^{-12k} = 0.75$$

$$\ln e^{-12k} = \ln 0.75$$

$$-12k = -0.288$$

$$k = 0.02$$

(b) $P_t = P_0 e^{-0.02t}$

$$40 = 80 e^{-0.02t}$$

$$e^{-0.02t} = 0.5$$

$$\ln e^{-0.02t} = \ln 0.5$$

$$-0.02t = -0.693$$

$$t = 34.7\,\text{h or } 34\,\text{h } 42\,\text{min}$$

C **Example 6**

From the experimental data given in the table:
(a) show that x and y are related by the formula
$y = kx^n$
(b) find the value of k and n, and state the
formula that connects x and y.

x	10.1	19.9	31	39.5
y	2.5	4.1	5.5	6.6

Solution
(a) Taking logarithms to base 10 of x and y gives:

$\log_{10} x$	1.0	1.3	1.5	1.6
$\log_{10} y$	0.40	0.61	0.74	0.82

These points lie on a straight line.
Hence, the formula connecting x and
y is of the form $y = kx^n$.

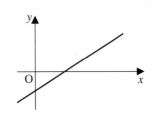

(b) Taking two points on the line $Y = nX + C$,
$Y = \log_{10} y$, $X = \log_{10} x$ and $C = \log_{10} k$.

$$Y = nX + C$$
$$0.61 = n1.3 + C$$
$$0.82 = n1.6 + C$$

Solving simultaneously gives $n = 0.7$ and $C = -0.3$.
Hence $k = 0.5$ and $y = 0.5x^{0.7}$

C **Example 7**

Part of the graph of $y = 3\log_4 (4x + 2)$ is
shown in the diagram. The graph crosses
the x-axis at the point A and crosses the
straight line $y = 6$ at the point B.
Find the x-coordinate of B.

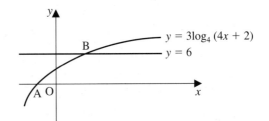

Solution
$y = 3\log_4 (4x + 2)$
At $y = 6$, $\quad y = 3\log_4 (4x + 2) = 6$
$$\log_4 (4x + 2) = 2$$
$$4x + 2 = 4^2$$
$$4x = 14$$
$$x = \frac{7}{2}$$

Revision exercise 15

U **1** Simplify
(a) $\log_2 16$
(b) $\log_5 125$
(c) $\log_4 4096$

U 2 Simplify

(a) $\log_2 8 + \log_2 4$ (b) $\log_a 12 + \log_a 3 - \log_a 4$

(c) $\log_3 9 + \log_3 27 - \log_3 \frac{1}{3}$ (d) $\frac{1}{4}\log_2 16$

(e) $2\log_3 9$ (f) $4\log_4 2 - \log_4 8$

(g) $10\log_5 3 - 2\log_5 1$ (h) $4\log_4 \frac{1}{2}$

U 3 Find an expression for the exact value of x

(a) $3^x = 7$ (b) $2^x = 11$ (c) $5^x = \frac{1}{10}$

U 4 Find an approximation for

(a) $\log_e 3$ (b) $\ln 5$ (c) $\dfrac{\ln 6}{\ln 4}$

U 5 Find an expression for the exact value of y

(a) $\log_8 y = 2.8$ (b) $\log_7 y = 0.8$ (c) $\log_3 y = -0.5$

U 6 Find an approximation for y

(a) $y = 5^{2.1}$ (b) $y = 8.5^{1.2}$ (c) $y = 3.5^{-1.2}$

C 7 Solve for x, $x > 0$

(a) $\log_5 (x^2 - 1) - \log_5 (x + 1) = 3$

(b) $\log_3 (x - 1) + \log_3 (x + 1) = 1$

C 8 For the formula $F(m) = 20e^{-m}$ find

(a) $F(0)$

(b) m such that $F(m) = \frac{1}{2}F(0)$.

C 9 For the formula $S = T10^{-kl}$, find k given that $l = 10$ when $S = 100T$.

C 10 The number of bacteria in a petri dish is given by the formula $B(t) = 20e^{1.2t}$, where t is time in hours.

(a) How many bacteria are there at time zero?

(b) How long will it take for the number of bacteria to triple?

C 11 The formula $A = A_0 e^{-kt}$ gives the amount of a radioactive substance after time t minutes. After 4 minutes 50 g is reduced to 45 g.

(a) Find the value of k to two significant figures.

(b) How long does it take for the substance to reduce to half its original weight?

C 12 The table below shows figures obtained from an experiment.

$\log_{10} x$	0.699	0.903	1.08	1.15	1.30
$\log_{10} y$	1.35	1.66	1.92	2.02	2.25

Show that a relationship of the form $y = ax^b$ exists and find approximate values for a and b.

C 13 For each line of best fit shown, $\log_{10} y$ is plotted against $\log_{10} x$. Express y in terms of x.

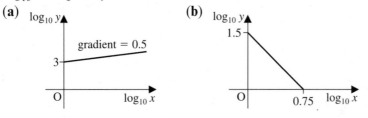

(a)   gradient = 0.5

(b)

C 14 For each line of best fit shown, $\log_{10} y$ is plotted against x. Express y in terms of x.

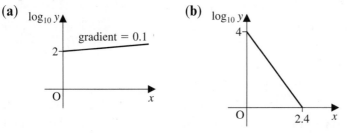

(a)   gradient = 0.1

(b)

C 15 The diagram shows the graph of $y = 3\log_2 4x$. The point A is where the graph cuts the x-axis and the point B is where it cuts the line $y = 9$. Find the coordinates of A and B.

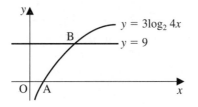

C 16 The diagram shows a sketch of the graph of $y = f(x)$, where $f(x) = a\log_2(x - b)$. Find the values of a and b.

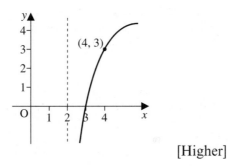

[Higher]

C 17 The diagram shows a sketch of the graph of $y = f(x)$, where $f(x) = \log_a(x + b)$. Find the values of a and b.

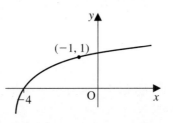

Test yourself	What to review

If your answer is incorrect:

U 1   Simplify

(a) $\log_a 15 - \log_a 3$

(a) $2\log_9 3 + \log_9 27$

Review Heinemann Higher Mathematics Chapter 15, pages 286 and 287

U 2   Find an expression for the exact value of x.

(a) $3^x = 13$

(a) $\log_{10} x = 2.9$

Review Heinemann Higher Mathematics Chapter 15, pages 288 and 289

U 3   Find an approximation for y.

(a) $y = \dfrac{\ln 13}{\ln 2}$

(a) $y = 5^{1.8}$

Review Heinemann Higher Mathematics Chapter 15, pages 280 and 281

C 4   In an experiment the data shown in the table was obtained.

$\log_{10} x$	0	0.176	0.301	0.477	0.602
$\log_{10} y$	0.875	1.40	1.78	2.31	2.68

Show that the relationship between y and x is of the form $y = kx^n$ and find the values of k and n.

Review Heinemann Higher Mathematics Chapter 15, pages 290 and 291

C 5   The diagram shows a sketch of $y = a\log_4(x + b)$. Find the values of a and b.

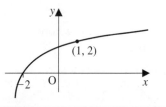

Review Heinemann Higher Mathematics Chapter 15, pages 295 and 296

Test yourself answers

1 (a) $\log_a 5$ (b) $\dfrac{5}{2}$ **2** (a) $\log_3 13$ (b) $10^{2.9}$ **3** (a) 3.7   (b) 18.1   **4** $k = 7.5, n = 3$ **5** $a = 2, b = 3$

16 The wave function

Key points to remember

1 $a \cos x + b \sin x$ can be written in the forms:

- $k \cos(x - \alpha)$
- $k \cos(x + \alpha)$
- $k \sin(x - \alpha)$
- $k \sin(x + \alpha)$

where $k = \sqrt{a^2 + b^2}$ and $\tan \alpha$ can be calculated using a and b. You must first expand $\cos(x \pm \alpha)$ or $\sin(x \pm \alpha)$ and then equate coefficients.

2 The maximum and minimum values of $a \cos x + b \sin x$ are given by the maximum and minimum values of any of:

- $k \cos(x - \alpha)$
- $k \cos(x + \alpha)$
- $k \sin(x - \alpha)$
- $k \sin(x - \alpha)$

3 The solutions of the equation $a \cos x + b \sin x = c$ can be obtained from any of the equations:

- $k \cos(x - \alpha) = c$
- $k \cos(x + \alpha) = c$
- $k \sin(x - \alpha) = c$
- $k \sin(x + \alpha) = c$

Outcome 4

Apply further trigonometric relationships.

Performance criteria

PC(a) Express $a \cos \theta + b \sin \theta$ in the form $r \cos(\theta \pm \alpha)$ or $r \sin(\theta \pm \alpha)$

U Example 1

Express $2 \sin x^\circ - 5 \cos x^\circ$ in the form $k \sin(x - \alpha)^\circ$, where $k > 0$ and $0 \leqslant \alpha \leqslant 360$. [Higher]

Solution

$$2 \sin x^\circ - 5 \cos x^\circ = k \sin(x - \alpha)^\circ$$
$$= k(\sin x^\circ \cos \alpha^\circ - \cos x^\circ \sin \alpha^\circ)$$
$$= k \cos \alpha^\circ \sin x^\circ - k \sin \alpha^\circ \cos x^\circ$$

Hence $k \cos \alpha^\circ = 2$

$k \sin \alpha^\circ = 5$

$k = \sqrt{2^2 + 5^2} = \sqrt{29}$

$\tan \alpha^\circ = \frac{5}{2}$

$\alpha = 68.2$

α° is in the first quadrant as both $\cos \alpha^\circ$ and $\sin \alpha^\circ$ are positive

S	A
✓	✓✓
	✓
T	C

$$2 \sin x^\circ - 5 \sin x^\circ = \sqrt{29} \sin(x - 68.2)^\circ$$

U Example 2

Express $3\cos x° - 4\sin x°$ in the form $k\cos(x - \alpha)°$ where $k > 0$ and $0 \leqslant \alpha \leqslant 360$.

Solution

$$3\cos x° - 4\sin x° = k\cos(x - \alpha)°$$
$$= k(\cos x° \cos \alpha° + \sin x° \sin \alpha°)$$
$$= k\cos \alpha° \cos x° + k\sin \alpha° \sin x°$$

Hence $k\cos \alpha° = 3$

$\qquad k\sin \alpha° = -4$

$\qquad\qquad k = \sqrt{3^2 + (-4)^2} = 5$

$\qquad\qquad \tan \alpha° = \dfrac{-4}{3}$

$\qquad\qquad\quad \alpha = 306.9$

α is in the fourth quadrant as $\cos \alpha°$ is positive and $\sin \alpha°$ is negative

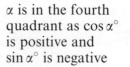

$$3\cos x° + 4\sin x° = 5\cos(x - 306.9)°$$

U Example 3

Express $\sqrt{3}\cos \theta - \sin \theta$ in the form $r\sin(\theta + \alpha)$ where $r > 0$ and $0 \leqslant \alpha \leqslant 2\pi$.

Solution

$$\sqrt{3}\cos \theta - \sin \theta = r\sin(\theta + \alpha)$$
$$= r(\sin \theta \cos \alpha + \cos \theta \sin \alpha)$$
$$= r\cos \alpha \sin \theta + r\sin \alpha \cos \theta$$

Hence $r\cos \alpha = -1$

$\qquad r\sin \alpha = \sqrt{3}$

$\qquad\qquad r = \sqrt{(-1)^2 + \sqrt{3}^2} = 2$

$\qquad\qquad \tan \alpha = \dfrac{\sqrt{3}}{-1}$

$\qquad\qquad\quad \alpha = \dfrac{2\pi}{3}$

α is in the second quadrant as $\cos \alpha$ is negative and $\sin \alpha$ is positive

$$\sqrt{3}\cos \theta - \sin \theta = 2\sin\left(\theta + \frac{2\pi}{3}\right)$$

C Example 4

When two sound waves are added together the volume, V, at any time, t seconds, is given by $V(t) = 40\cos t° + 20\sin t°$. Find the maximum volume and the time t at which this maximum first occurs.

Solution

$$40\cos t° + 20\sin t° = k\cos(t - \alpha)°$$
$$= k(\cos t° \cos \alpha° + \sin t° \sin \alpha°)$$
$$= k\cos \alpha° \cos t° + k\sin \alpha° \sin t°$$

Hence $k \cos \alpha° = 40$

$k \sin \alpha° = 20$

$k = \sqrt{40^2 + 20^2} = 20\sqrt{5}$

$\tan \alpha° = \dfrac{20}{40}$

$\alpha = 26.6$

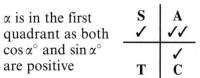

α is in the first quadrant as both $\cos \alpha°$ and $\sin \alpha°$ are positive

$V(t) = 40 \cos t° + 20 \sin t°$

$\qquad = 20\sqrt{5} \cos(t - 26.6)°$

The maximum value of $\cos(t - 26.6)°$ is 1

Hence the maximum value of $20\sqrt{5} \cos(t - 26.6)°$ is $20\sqrt{5}$

This maximum occurs when $\cos(t - 26.6)° = 1$

$\qquad\qquad\qquad\qquad$ so $(t - 26.6) = 0$

$\qquad\qquad\qquad\qquad\qquad\qquad t = 26.6$

The maximum value is $20\sqrt{5}$ and first occurs at 26.6 seconds.

C   Example 5
Solve algebraically $\sqrt{2} \sin \theta - \sqrt{6} \cos \theta = 2$ for $0 \leqslant \theta \leqslant 2\pi$.

Solution

$$\sqrt{2} \sin \theta - \sqrt{6} \cos \theta = k \cos(\theta - \alpha)$$
$$= k(\cos \theta \cos \alpha + \sin \theta \sin \alpha)$$
$$= k \cos \alpha \cos \theta + k \sin \alpha \sin \theta$$

Hence $k \cos \alpha = -\sqrt{6}$

$k \sin \alpha = \sqrt{2}$

$k = \sqrt{(\sqrt{2})^2 + (-\sqrt{6})^2} = 2\sqrt{2}$

$\tan \alpha = \dfrac{\sqrt{2}}{-\sqrt{6}} = \dfrac{-1}{\sqrt{3}}$

$\alpha = \dfrac{5\pi}{6}$

α is in the second quadrant as $\cos \alpha$ is negative and $\sin \alpha$ is positive

$\sqrt{2} \sin \theta - \sqrt{6} \cos \theta = 2$

$2\sqrt{2} \cos\left(\theta - \dfrac{5\pi}{6}\right) = 2$

$\cos\left(\theta - \dfrac{5\pi}{6}\right) = \dfrac{1}{\sqrt{2}}$

$\left(\theta - \dfrac{5\pi}{6}\right) = \dfrac{\pi}{4}$ or $\dfrac{-\pi}{4}$

$\left(\text{Since } 0 \leqslant \theta \leqslant 2\pi, \\ -\dfrac{5\pi}{6} \leqslant \theta - \dfrac{5\pi}{6} \leqslant \dfrac{7\pi}{6}\right)$

$\theta = \dfrac{\pi}{4} + \dfrac{5\pi}{6}$ or $\dfrac{-\pi}{4} + \dfrac{5\pi}{6}$

$\theta = \dfrac{13\pi}{12}$ or $\dfrac{7\pi}{12}$

C Example 6

A research student observing waves in a tank uses the formula $h = 1.5 + 2\cos 30t° - \sin 30t°$, where h is the height of the wave in metres and t is the time in seconds after the start of the experiment. The wave may overflow the tank if its height exceeds 3.5 metres.

Between which times is the wave first in danger of overflowing?

Solution

$$2\cos 30t° - \sin 30t° = k\cos(30t - \alpha)°$$
$$= k(\cos 30t° \cos \alpha° + \sin 30t° \sin \alpha°)$$
$$= k\cos \alpha° \cos 30t° + k\sin \alpha° \sin 30t°$$

Hence $k\cos \alpha° = 2$
$$k\sin \alpha° = -1$$
$$k = \sqrt{2^2 + (-1)^2} = \sqrt{5}$$
$$\tan \alpha° = \frac{-1}{2}$$
$$\alpha = 333$$

α is in the fourth quadrant as $\cos \alpha°$ is positive and $\sin \alpha°$ is negative

S	A
	✓
✓	✓✓
T	C

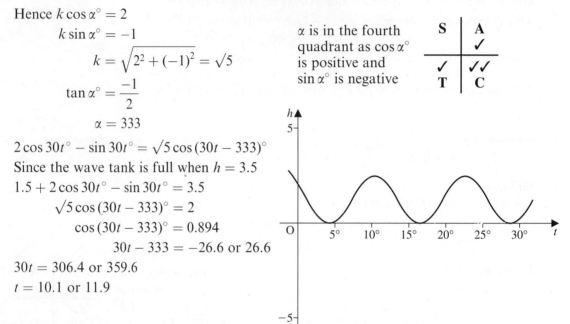

$$2\cos 30t° - \sin 30t° = \sqrt{5}\cos(30t - 333)°$$

Since the wave tank is full when $h = 3.5$
$$1.5 + 2\cos 30t° - \sin 30t° = 3.5$$
$$\sqrt{5}\cos(30t - 333)° = 2$$
$$\cos(30t - 333)° = 0.894$$
$$30t - 333 = -26.6 \text{ or } 26.6$$
$$30t = 306.4 \text{ or } 359.6$$
$$t = 10.1 \text{ or } 11.9$$

The wave is first in danger of overflowing between 10.1 and 11.9 seconds after the start of the experiment.

Revision exercise 16

U 1 Express the following in the form $k\cos(x - a)°$ where $k > 0$ and $0 \leqslant a \leqslant 360$.
   (a) $\cos x° + \sin x°$ (b) $4\cos x° - 3\sin x°$

U 2 Express the following in the form $k\cos(x + a)°$ where $k > 0$ and $0 \leqslant a \leqslant 360$.
   (a) $\sqrt{3}\cos x° + \sin x°$ (b) $3\sin x° - 2\cos x°$

U 3 Express the following in the form $k\sin(x - a)°$ where $k > 0$ and $0 \leqslant a \leqslant 360$.
   (a) $2.5\sin x° + 5\cos x°$ (b) $\sqrt{6}\cos x° - \sqrt{2}\sin x°$

U 4 Express the following in the form $k\sin(x + a)°$ where $k > 0$ and $0 \leqslant a \leqslant 360$.
   (a) $5\cos x° - 2\sin x°$ (b) $8\sin x° - 5\cos x°$

U **5** Express the following in the form $r\cos(\theta - \alpha)$ where $r > 0$ and $0 \leqslant \alpha \leqslant 2\pi$.
  (a) $3\sin\theta - 3\cos\theta$ (b) $2\cos\theta - \sqrt{12}\sin\theta$

U **6** Express the following in the form $r\sin(\theta + \alpha)$ where $r > 0$ and $0 \leqslant \alpha \leqslant 2\pi$.
  (a) $\sqrt{3}\cos\theta - \sin\theta$ (b) $-2\cos\theta - 2\sin\theta$

C **7** Express $4\cos 2x° - 3\sin 2x°$ in the form $k\sin(2x - a)°$ where $k > 0$ and $0 \leqslant a \leqslant 360$.

C **8** Express $5\cos 8\theta + \sin 8\theta$ in the form $r\sin(8\theta + \alpha)$ where $r > 0$ and $0 \leqslant \alpha \leqslant 2\pi$.

C **9** Express the following in the form $k\cos(x - a)°$ where $k > 0$ and $0 \leqslant a \leqslant 360$ and hence find the maximum value of each.
  (a) $10\cos x° + 5\sin x°$ (b) $5\sin x° - 4\cos x°$

C **10** Express the following in the form $r\cos(\theta - \alpha)$ where $r > 0$ and $0 \leqslant \alpha \leqslant 2\pi$ and hence find the minimum value of each.
  (a) $\sin\theta - \sqrt{3}\cos\theta$ (b) $10\cos\theta - 8\sin\theta$

C **11** (a) Express $25\cos \omega t + 25\sin \omega t$ in the form $r\sin(\omega t + \alpha)$ where $r > 0$ and $0 \leqslant \alpha \leqslant 2\pi$.
  (b) Hence find the maximum value of
    $100 + 25\cos \omega t + 25\sin \omega t$.

C **12** $f(x) = 2\cos x° + 3\sin x°$.
  (a) Express $f(x)$ in the form $k\cos(x - \alpha)°$ where $k > 0$ and $0 \leqslant \alpha < 360$.
  (b) Hence solve algebraically $f(x) = 0.5$ for $0 \leqslant x < 360$.
                    [Higher]

C **13** Solve each equation algebraically for $0 \leqslant x \leqslant 360$.
  (a) $3\cos x° + 2\sin x° = 1$ (b) $4.5\sin x° + 6\cos x° = 7.5$

C **14** Solve the equation $5\sqrt{3}\sin\theta - 5\cos\theta = 5$ algebraically for $0 \leqslant \theta \leqslant 2\pi$.

C **15** The displacement, d units, of a wave after t seconds is given by the formula $d = \cos 20t° + \sqrt{3}\sin 20t°$.
  (a) Express d in the form $k\cos(20t - \alpha)°$, where $k > 0$ and $0 \leqslant \alpha \leqslant 360$.
  (b) Sketch the graph of d for $0 \leqslant t \leqslant 18$.
  (c) Find, correct to one decimal place, the values of t, $0 \leqslant t \leqslant 18$, for which the displacement is 1.5 units.
                    [Higher]

C **16** The formula $d(t) = 100 + 150\cos 30t° - 100\sin 30t°$ gives an approximation to the depth, in centimetres, of water in a harbour t hours after midnight.
  (a) Express $f(t) = 150\cos 30t° - 100\sin 30t°$ in the form $k\cos(30t - \alpha)°$ and state the values of k and α, where $0 \leqslant \alpha \leqslant 360$.
  (b) Use your result from (a) to help you sketch the graph of $f(t)$ for $0 \leqslant t \leqslant 24$.
  (c) Hence, on a separate diagram, sketch the graph of $d(t)$ for $0 \leqslant t \leqslant 24$.
  (d) When is the first 'low water' time at the harbour?

    (e) The local fishing fleet needs at least 2 metres depth of water to enter the harbour without risk of running aground. Between what times must it avoid entering the harbour?

C   **17**   The frequency, f hertz, of the sound of a car alarm t seconds after it starts to sound is given by
$f = 2500 - 200 \sin 120t° + 200\sqrt{3} \cos 120t°.$
    (a) Express f in the form $f = 2500 + k \sin(120t + \alpha)°$ where $k > 0$ and $0 \leqslant \alpha \leqslant 180$.
    (b) Hence, sketch the graph of f for $0 \leqslant t \leqslant 6$.
    (c) If the frequency rises above 2800 hertz, the alarm may cause noise pollution. Between which times is the alarm sounding above this frequency?

Test yourself	**What to review**
	If your answer is incorrect:
U **1** Express $2\cos x° - 3\sin x°$ in the form $k\cos(x - \alpha)°$ where $k > 0$ and $0 \leqslant \alpha \leqslant 360$.	*Review Heinemann Higher Mathematics Chapter 16, pages 303 and 304*
U **2** Express $2\sin x° - 5\cos x°$ in the form $k\sin(x - \alpha)°$, where $k > 0$ and $0 \leqslant \alpha \leqslant 360$.	*Review Heinemann Higher Mathematics Chapter 16, page 305*
C **3** Solve algebraically $2\cos\theta - 2\sqrt{3}\sin\theta = 2$ for $0 \leqslant \theta \leqslant 2\pi$.	*Review Heinemann Higher Mathematics Chapter 16, pages 308 to 310*
C **4** Express $15\sin\theta - 5\cos\theta$ in the form $r\cos(\theta - \alpha)$ where $r > 0$ and $0 \leqslant \alpha \leqslant 2\pi$ and hence find the minimum value.	*Review Heinemann Higher Mathematics Chapter 16, pages 307 and 308*

C **5** The formula $d(t) = 12 + 6\cos 10t° + 2\sin 10t°$ gives an approximation to the depth, in centimetres, of water in a test tank t minutes after the start of an experiment.
  (a) Express $f(t) = 6\cos 10t° + 2\sin 10t°$ in the form $k\cos(10t - \alpha)°$ and state the values of k and α, where $0 \leqslant \alpha \leqslant 360$.
  (b) Use your result from part (a) to help you sketch the graph of $f(t)$ for $0 \leqslant t \leqslant 72$.
  (c) Hence, on a separate diagram, sketch the graph of $d(t)$ for $0 \leqslant t \leqslant 72$.
  (d) How long after the start of the experiment does the water reach a minimum?
  (e) Between what times is the depth of water greater than 16 centimetres?
	Review Heinemann Higher Mathematics Chapter 16, pages 310 to 313

Test yourself answers

1 $\sqrt{13}\cos(x - 303.7)°$ **2** $\sqrt{29}\sin(x - 68.2)°$ **3** $0, \dfrac{4\pi}{3}, 2\pi$

4 $\sqrt{250}\cos(\theta - 1.89)$; minimum value $= -\sqrt{250}$ **5** (a) $2\sqrt{10}\cos(10t - 18.4)°$

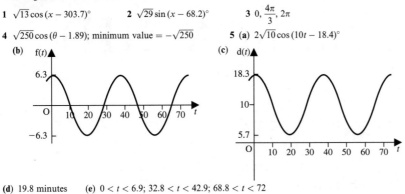

(b)

(c)

(d) 19.8 minutes   (e) $0 < t < 6.9$; $32.8 < t < 42.9$; $68.8 < t < 72$

Specimen
Unit assessment A–1(H)

Outcome 1

1 A line passes through the points $(4, -1)$ and $(-2, 2)$.
Find the equation of this line. (3 marks)

2 A line makes an angle of $70°$ with the positive
direction of the x-axis, as shown in the diagram,
where the scales on the axes are equal.
Find the gradient of the line.

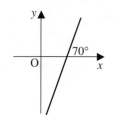

(1 mark)

3 (a) Write down the gradient of a line parallel to $y = 3x + 1$. (1 mark)
(b) Write down the gradient of a line perpendicular to
$y = 3x + 1$. (1 mark)

Outcome 2

4 The diagram shows part of the graph of $y = f(x)$.
(a) Draw the graph of $y = -f(x)$. (1 mark)
(b) Draw the graph of $y = f(x + 2)$. (1 mark)

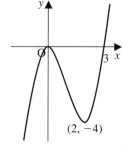

5 The diagrams below show parts of the graphs of
(a) $y = \sin x°$ and a related function.
(b) $y = \cos x°$ and a related function.
Write down the equation of each of the related functions.

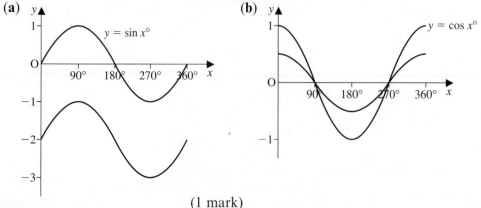

(1 mark)   (1 mark)

6 The graph of $y = 4^x$ is shown below.
Write down the equation of the graph of the exponential function
of the form $y = a^x$ which passes through the point (2, 4).   (1 mark)

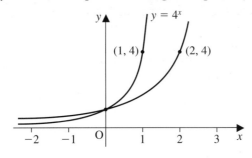

7 The diagram below shows part of the graph of the
function $y = 5^x$ and its inverse function.
Write down the equation of the inverse function.   (1 mark)

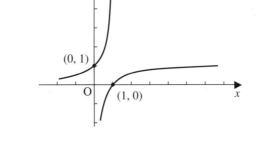

8 (a) Two functions f and g are given by $f(x) = x^2$ and
$g(x) = 3x + 1$. Obtain an expression for $f(g(x))$.   (1 mark)
(b) Functions h and k, defined on suitable domains, are given by
$h(x) = 2x$ and $k(x) = \sin x$. Find $k(h(x))$.   (1 mark)

Outcome 3

9 Given $y = \dfrac{x^4 - 1}{x^2}$, find $\dfrac{dy}{dx}$.   (4 marks)

10 The diagram shows a sketch of a curve with equation
$y = x^2 - 10x + 24$ with a tangent drawn at the point (7, 3).
Find the gradient of this tangent.   (4 marks)

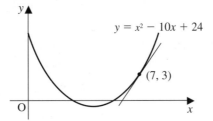

11 Find the coordinates of the stationary points of the curve with
equation $y = \frac{1}{3}x^3 + 2x^2 + 3x + 4$. Using differentiation determine
their nature.   (8 marks)

Outcome 4

12 In a pond one-fifth of the existing tadpoles are eaten by predators each day but during the night 2000 tadpoles are hatched. There are u_n tadpoles at the start of a particular day.

(a) Write down a recurrence relation for u_{n+1}, the number of tadpoles at the start of the next day. (1 mark)

(b) Find the limit of the sequence generated by this recurrence relation and explain what the limit means in the context of this question. (3 marks)

Specimen
Unit assessment B–1(H)

Outcome 1

1 Find the equation of the line which passes through the points
(2, −3) and (4, −5). (3 marks)

2 The line AB makes an angle of 38° with
the positive direction of the x-axis,
as shown in the diagram.
Find the gradient of AB.

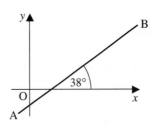

(1 mark)

3 (a) Write down the gradient of a line parallel to $y = \frac{1}{2}x - 1$. (1 mark)

   (b) Write down the gradient of a line perpendicular to
$y = \frac{1}{2}x - 1$. (1 mark)

Outcome 2

4 (a) The graph of $y = f(x)$ is shown in the diagram.
    (i) Sketch the graph of $y = f(x - 2)$. (1 mark)
    (ii) Sketch the graph of $y = 1 - f(x)$. (1 mark)

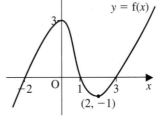

   (b) The diagram shows the graph of $y = f(x)$
which is of the form $y = a\sin x°$.
    (i) State the value of a. (1 mark)
    (ii) Sketch the graph of $y = f(x) - 2$. (1 mark)

5 (a) The diagram shows a graph of the
form $y = b^x$.
Find the value of b. (1 mark)

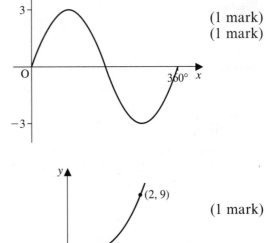

(b) The diagram shows part of the graph of the function $y = 3^x$ and its inverse function. Write down the equation of the inverse function.

(1 mark)

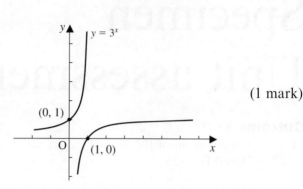

6 (a) The functions f and g are defined as $f(x) = 2x^2$ and $g(x) = x + 4$. Express $f(g(x))$ in terms of x.

(1 mark)

(b) The functions f and g are defined as $f(x) = 4x$ and $g(x) = \cos x$. Express $g(f(x))$ in terms of x.

(1 mark)

Outcome 3

7 Differentiate the following with respect to x.

(a) $(x - 3)^2$

(2 marks)

(b) $\dfrac{x^{\frac{3}{2}} + 1}{x}$

(2 marks)

8 The diagram shows a sketch of the curve with equation $y = x^2 - x - 12$ with a tangent drawn at the point $(5, 8)$. Find the equation of this tangent.

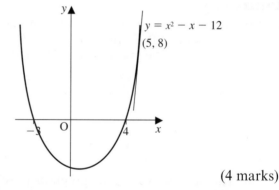

(4 marks)

9 Find the stationary values of the function $f(x) = 2x^3 + 3x^2 - 12x + 5$ and determine their nature.

(8 marks)

Outcome 4

10 In a controlled experiment, a biologist discovers that 100 aphids are born each week. A parasite is introduced which kills 30% of the aphids each week.

(a) If the number of aphids at the start of week n is defined as u_n write down a recurrence relation for u_{n+1}.

(1 mark)

(b) Find the limit of this recurrence relation and explain what the limit means in the context of the question.

(3 marks)

Specimen
Unit assessment A–2(H)

Outcome 1

1 Show that $(x + 2)$ is a factor of $f(x) = x^3 + 3x^2 - 4x - 12$, and express $f(x)$ in fully factorised form. (4 marks)

2 Use the discriminant to determine the nature of the roots of the equation $5x^2 - 3x + 2 = 0$. (2 marks)

Outcome 2

3 Find $\displaystyle\int \frac{2}{x^4}\, dx$. (3 marks)

4 Calculate the shaded area shown in the diagram.

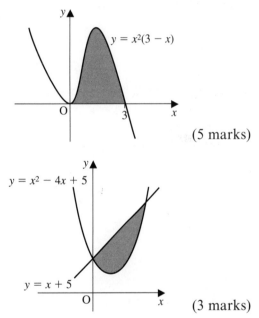

$y = x^2(3 - x)$

(5 marks)

5 The diagram shows the line with equation $y = x + 5$ and the curve with equation $y = x^2 - 4x + 5$.
Write down the integral which represents the shaded area.
Do **not** carry out the integration.

$y = x^2 - 4x + 5$

$y = x + 5$

(3 marks)

Outcome 3

6 Solve algebraically the equation $2\cos 2x = \sqrt{3}$ for $0 \leqslant x < \pi$. (3 marks)

7 The diagram shows two right-angled triangles ABC and DEF.

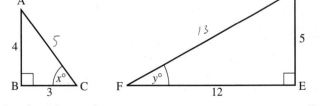

(a) Write down the values of $\sin x°$ and $\cos y°$. (2 marks)

(b) By expanding $\cos(x - y)°$ show that the **exact** value of $\cos(x - y)°$ is $\frac{56}{65}$. (2 marks)

8 (a) Express $\sin x° \cos 40° + \cos x° \sin 40°$ in the form $\sin (A + B)°$. (1 mark)

(b) Use the result of **(a)** to solve the equation

$\sin x° \cos 40° + \cos x° \sin 40° = \frac{3}{4}$ for $0 \leqslant x < 180°$. (4 marks)

Outcome 4

9 (a) A circle has radius 6 units and centre $(8, -2)$. Write down the equation of the circle. (2 marks)

(b) A circle has equation $x^2 + y^2 - 6x + 8y - 11 = 0$. Write down its radius and the coordinates of its centre. (3 marks)

10 Show that the straight line with equation $y = 3 - 2x$ is a tangent to the circle with equation $x^2 + y^2 + 2x - 4 = 0$. (5 marks)

11 The point P$(1, -6)$ lies on the circle with the centre $(4, -1)$, as shown in the diagram. Find the equation of the tangent at P.

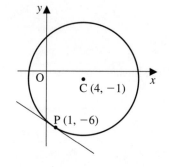

(4 marks)

Specimen
Unit assessment B–2(H)

Outcome 1

1 (a) Show that $(x-1)$ is a factor of $3x^3 - 7x^2 - 3x + 7$.   (2 marks)
  (b) Hence, or otherwise, fully factorise $3x^3 - 7x^2 - 3x + 7$.   (2 marks)

2 Show that the quadratic equation $2x^2 - 3x + 7 = 0$ has no real
roots.   (2 marks)

Outcome 2

3 Find $\displaystyle\int \left(2x^2 + \frac{4}{\sqrt{x}}\right) dx$.   (3 marks)

4 Find $\displaystyle\int \frac{x^2 + 4}{x^2} \, dx$.   (2 marks)

5 Calculate the area of the shaded
region in the diagram.

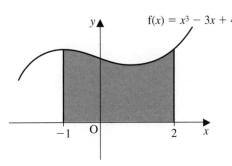

     (4 marks)

6 Find the area enclosed by the graphs of $y = 2x$ and $y = 15 - x^2$.   (3 marks)

Outcome 3

7 The diagram shows the cross-section of an adjustable
ramp which is made from two right-angled triangles,
ABD and DBC. Angle $\mathbf{DBC} = \alpha°$ and angle $\mathbf{ABD} = \beta°$.
Find the exact value of $\cos{(\alpha + \beta)}°$.

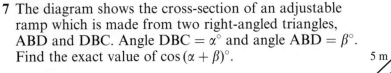

     (4 marks)

8 (a) Express $\sin x° \cos 10° - \cos x° \sin 10°$ in the form $\sin{(A - B)}°$.   (1 mark)
  (b) Use the result of **(a)** to solve the equation
     $\sin x° \cos 10° - \cos x° \sin 10° = \frac{2}{5}$ for $0 \leqslant x < 180$.   (3 marks)

9 Solve $\cos 2x° - \cos x° = 0$ for $0 \leqslant x \leqslant 360$.   (3 marks)

Outcome 4

10 A circle has equation $x^2 + y^2 + 4x + 6y - 12 = 0$. Find the coordinates of its centre and the length of its radius.

(2 marks)

11 A circle has radius 5 units and centre $(-5, 2)$. Write down the equation of the circle.

(3 marks)

12 Show that the line with equation $y = 5 + 2x$ is a tangent to the circle with equation $x^2 + y^2 = 5$.

(5 marks)

13 The point A$(3, -2)$ lies on the circle $x^2 + y^2 - 4x - 1 = 0$. Find the equation of the tangent to the circle at A.

(3 marks)

Specimen
Unit assessment A–3(H)

Outcome 1

1 (a) A, B and C have coordinates (1, 2, 3), (4, −4, 12) and (3, −2, 9).

    (i) Write down the components of $\overrightarrow{AC}$.   (1 mark)

    (ii) Hence show that the points A, B and C are collinear.   (3 marks)

  (b) The point L divides KM in the ratio
2:1, as shown in the diagram.
Find the coordinates of L.

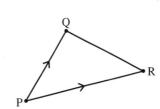

    (3 marks)

2 The diagram shows triangle PQR where

$$\overrightarrow{PQ} = \begin{pmatrix} 2 \\ -1 \\ -2 \end{pmatrix} \text{ and } \overrightarrow{PR} = \begin{pmatrix} -3 \\ 0 \\ 4 \end{pmatrix}.$$

  (a) Find the value of $\overrightarrow{PQ}.\overrightarrow{PR}$.   (1 mark)

  (b) Use the result of **(a)** to find the size of angle QPR.   (4 marks)

Outcome 2

3 (a) Differentiate $y = -2 \sin x$ with respect to x.   (1 mark)

  (b) Given $y = \frac{1}{3} \cos x$, find $\dfrac{dy}{dx}$ (1 mark)

4 Find f′(x) when f$(x) = (4x + 3)^3$.   (2 marks)

5 (a) Find $\displaystyle\int -2 \cos x \, dx$ (2 marks)

  (b) Integrate $y = \frac{3}{4} \sin x$ with respect to x.   (1 mark)

  (c) Evaluate $\displaystyle\int_1^3 (x - 1)^3 \, dx$ (4 marks)

Outcome 3

6 (a) Simplify $\log_a 10 - \log_a 2$.   (1 mark)

  (b) Simplify $4 \log_8 2 + \log_8 4$.   (3 marks)

7 (a) Given that $3^x = 8$, find an expression for the **exact** value of x. (1 mark)

(b) If $x = \dfrac{\log_e 5}{\log_e 2}$, find an approximation for x. (1 mark)

(c) Given that $\log_{10} y = 4.1$, write down an expression for the **exact** value of y. (1 mark)

(d) If $y = 10^{1.9}$, find an approximation for y. (1 mark)

Outcome 4

8 Express $3\cos x° + 5\sin x°$ in the form $k\cos(x - a)°$ where $k > 0$ and $0 \leqslant a < 360$. (5 marks)

Specimen
Unit assessment B–3(H)

Outcome 1

1 A(3, −2, −2), P(5, −4, −1) and R(9, −8, 1) are three points in space. Prove that A, P and R are collinear. (4 marks)

2 G is the point (7, −5, 1) and T is the point (1, 1, 7). Find the coordinates of B, which divides GT in the ratio 1:2. (3 marks)

3 $\overrightarrow{QP} = 5\mathbf{i} + 2\mathbf{j} + 2\mathbf{k}$ and $\overrightarrow{QR} = 2\mathbf{i} + 4\mathbf{j} + 4\mathbf{k}$.

  (a) Calculate $\overrightarrow{QP}.\overrightarrow{QR}$. (1 mark)

  (b) Find the value of $\cos P\widehat{Q}R$. (4 marks)

4 $\mathbf{p} = \begin{pmatrix} -2 \\ 8 \\ -2 \end{pmatrix}$ and $\mathbf{r} = \begin{pmatrix} -4 \\ -2 \\ -4 \end{pmatrix}$.

  Show that $\mathbf{p}$ and $\mathbf{r}$ are perpendicular. (2 marks)

Outcome 2

5 Differentiate $f(x) = 5\sin x + 3\cos x$. (2 marks)

6 (a) Given that $h(x) = (5 + 4x)^3$ find $h'(x)$. (2 marks)

  (b) Differentiate $\sin 3x + \cos^2 x$ with respect to x. (2 marks)

7 Find:

  (a) $\displaystyle\int_0^2 (x+1)^4 \, dx$ (3 marks)

  (b) $\displaystyle\int 4\cos x - 2\sin x \, dx$ (2 marks)

Outcome 3

8 Simplify

  (a) $\log_{10} 4 + \log_{10} 5 - \log_{10} 2$ (1 mark)

  (b) $4\log_3 3 - 2\log_3 9$ (3 marks)

9 (a) Solve, for $x > 0$, $3\log_a x + \log_a 3 = \log_a 2 + \log_a 12$ (2 marks)

  (b) Solve $e^{2x} = 18$ (2 marks)

Outcome 4

10 $\sqrt{3}\cos x° - \sin x°$ can be written in the form $k\cos(x + \alpha)°$ where $k > 0$ and $0 < \alpha < 360$. Find the values of k and α. (5 marks)

Formulae list

The equation $x^2 + y^2 + 2gx + 2fy + c = 0$ represents a circle centre $(-g, -f)$ and radius $\sqrt{(g^2 + f^2 - c)}$.

The equation $(x - a)^2 + (y - b)^2 = r^2$ represents a circle centre (a, b) and radius r.

Scalar product: $\mathbf{a} \cdot \mathbf{b} = |\mathbf{a}|\,|\mathbf{b}| \cos\theta$, where θ is the angle between $\mathbf{a}$ and $\mathbf{b}$

   or

   $\mathbf{a} \cdot \mathbf{b} = a_1 b_1 + a_2 b_2 + a_3 b_3$ where $\mathbf{a} = \begin{pmatrix} a_1 \\ a_2 \\ a_3 \end{pmatrix}$ and $\mathbf{b} = \begin{pmatrix} b_1 \\ b_2 \\ b_3 \end{pmatrix}$.

Trigonometric formulae:

$$\sin(A \pm B) = \sin A \cos B \pm \cos A \sin B$$
$$\cos(A \pm B) = \cos A \cos B \mp \sin A \sin B$$
$$\cos 2A = \cos^2 A - \sin^2 A$$
$$= 2\cos^2 A - 1$$
$$= 1 - 2\sin^2 A$$
$$\sin 2A = 2 \sin A \cos A$$

Table of standard derivatives:

$f(x)$	$f'(x)$
$\sin ax$	$a\cos ax$
$\cos ax$	$-a\sin ax$

Table of standard integrals:

$f(x)$	$\displaystyle\int f(x)\,dx$
$\sin ax$	$-\dfrac{1}{a}\cos ax + C$
$\cos ax$	$\dfrac{1}{a}\sin ax + C$

Specimen
Course assessment A

PAPER I
Calculators may not be used in this paper.
Answers obtained from scale drawings receive no credit.

1 L(-5, -1), M(1, 4) and N(3, -5) are the vertices of triangle LMN as shown in the diagram. Find the equation of MP, the altitude from M.

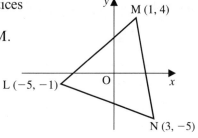

(3 marks)

2 A sequence is defined by the recurrence relation $u_{n+1} = 0.4u_n - 1$, with first term u_1.
   (a) Explain why this sequence has a limit as n tends to infinity. (1 mark)
   (b) Find the **exact** value of this limit. (2 marks)

3 (a) Show that $(x - 1)$ is a factor of $f(x) = 2x^3 + 5x^2 - 4x - 3$ and find the other factors. (3 marks)
   (b) Write down the coordinates of the points at which the graph of $y = f(x)$ meets the axes. (1 mark)
   (c) Find the stationary points of $y = f(x)$ and determine the nature of each. (5 marks)
   (d) Sketch the graph of $y = f(x)$. (1 mark)

4 If $x°$ is an acute angle such that $\tan x° = \frac{5}{12}$ show that the exact value of $\cos(x - 60)°$ is $\dfrac{5\sqrt{3} + 12}{26}$. (3 marks)

5 The diagram shows a 3-D art design with each end-point positioned in space relative to an origin.
   (a) Show that the cosine of angle UTS is $\frac{1}{2}$. (5 marks)
   (b) M is the mid-point of ST, and P divides UM in the ratio $2:1$.
      (i) Find the coordinates of P.
      (ii) Show that S, T and U are equidistant from P. (6 marks)

6 The diagram shows two circles with centres lying on a horizontal line. The equation of the larger circle is $x^2 + y^2 - 12x - 6y + 36 = 0$. Find the equation of the smaller circle. (5 marks)

7 Evaluate $\int_{-\sqrt{2}}^{0} t(t^2 - 2)\,dt$ and draw a sketch to illustrate the area

represented by this integral.   (5 marks)

8 Sketch the graph of $y = 3\cos(x + 45)°$ for $0 \leqslant x \leqslant 360$.   (4 marks)

9 Find $\dfrac{dy}{dx}$ given that $y = \sqrt{2 - \sin x}$.   (3 marks)

10 Part of the graph of $y = 3\log_4(3x + 4)$ is shown in the diagram.

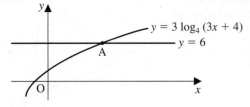

This graph crosses the straight line $y = 6$ at the point A.
Find the x-coordinate of A.   (3 marks)

PAPER II
Calculators may be used in this paper.
Answers obtained from scale drawings receive no credit.

1 PQRS is a parallelogram.
P, Q and R have coordinates $(-1, 1)$, $(6, 2)$ and $(7, -4)$.
Find the equation of SR.   (3 marks)

2 Crops are sprayed monthly with a pesticide called Bugoff, which
destroys 70% of all pests.
Between sprayings it is estimated 350 new pests invade the crop.
The pesticide Nobug destroys 90% of existing pests but 400 new
pests invade between sprayings.
Which pesticide is more effective in the long term?   (5 marks)

3 (a) Show that the function $f(x) = 3x^2 + 30x + 73$ can be written
   in the form $f(x) = a(x + b)^2 + c$ where a, b and c are
   constants.   (3 marks)
   (b) Hence, or otherwise, find the coordinates of the turning point
   of the function f.   (1 mark)

4 In the diagram the straight line AB is a
tangent to the curve $y = x^3 - x^2 - 4x + 1$
at the point A$(1, -3)$.
   (a) Find the equation of the tangent at A.   (3 marks)
   (b) Hence find the coordinates of B.   (4 marks)
   (c) Find the area of the shaded part
   between the curve and the line.

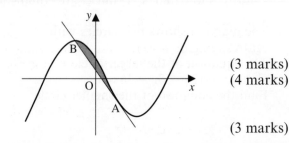

(3 marks)

5 The diagram shows two concentric circles.
The equation of the larger circle is
$x^2 + y^2 - 2x - 6y - 26 = 0$.
The line PQ is a tangent to the smaller
circle and has equation $y = 7$.

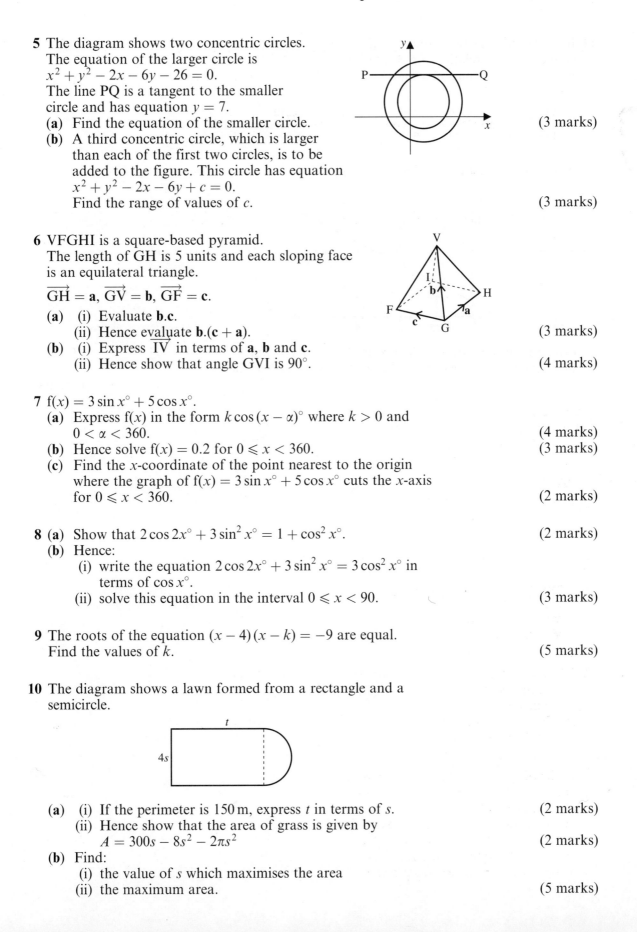

(a) Find the equation of the smaller circle.   (3 marks)
(b) A third concentric circle, which is larger
than each of the first two circles, is to be
added to the figure. This circle has equation
$x^2 + y^2 - 2x - 6y + c = 0$.
Find the range of values of c.   (3 marks)

6 VFGHI is a square-based pyramid.
The length of GH is 5 units and each sloping face
is an equilateral triangle.

$\overrightarrow{GH} = \mathbf{a}$, $\overrightarrow{GV} = \mathbf{b}$, $\overrightarrow{GF} = \mathbf{c}$.

(a) (i) Evaluate $\mathbf{b}.\mathbf{c}$.
(ii) Hence evaluate $\mathbf{b}.(\mathbf{c} + \mathbf{a})$.   (3 marks)
(b) (i) Express $\overrightarrow{IV}$ in terms of $\mathbf{a}$, $\mathbf{b}$ and $\mathbf{c}$.
(ii) Hence show that angle GVI is $90°$.   (4 marks)

7 $f(x) = 3 \sin x° + 5 \cos x°$.
(a) Express $f(x)$ in the form $k \cos (x - \alpha)°$ where $k > 0$ and
$0 < \alpha < 360$.   (4 marks)
(b) Hence solve $f(x) = 0.2$ for $0 \leqslant x < 360$.   (3 marks)
(c) Find the x-coordinate of the point nearest to the origin
where the graph of $f(x) = 3 \sin x° + 5 \cos x°$ cuts the x-axis
for $0 \leqslant x < 360$.   (2 marks)

8 (a) Show that $2 \cos 2x° + 3 \sin^2 x° = 1 + \cos^2 x°$.   (2 marks)
(b) Hence:
(i) write the equation $2 \cos 2x° + 3 \sin^2 x° = 3 \cos^2 x°$ in
terms of $\cos x°$.
(ii) solve this equation in the interval $0 \leqslant x < 90$.   (3 marks)

9 The roots of the equation $(x - 4)(x - k) = -9$ are equal.
Find the values of k.   (5 marks)

10 The diagram shows a lawn formed from a rectangle and a
semicircle.

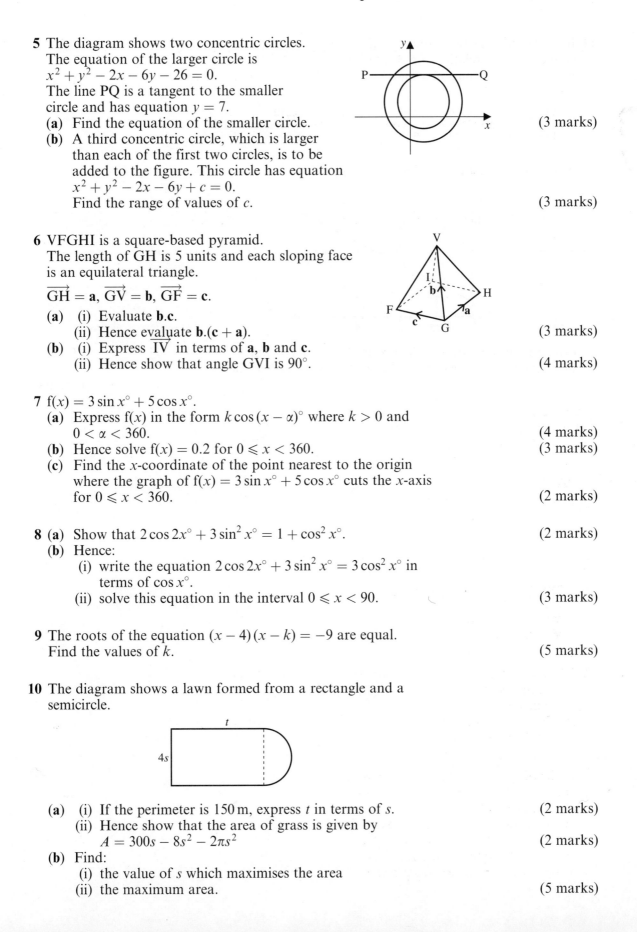

(a) (i) If the perimeter is 150 m, express t in terms of s.   (2 marks)
(ii) Hence show that the area of grass is given by
$A = 300s - 8s^2 - 2\pi s^2$ (2 marks)
(b) Find:
(i) the value of s which maximises the area
(ii) the maximum area.   (5 marks)

11 In an experiment two values, x and y, are thought to be
connected by a relationship of the form $y = ax^b$.
By taking logarithms of x and y the table below was constructed.

$X(= \ln x)$	0.916	1.308	1.629	2.219
$Y(= \ln y)$	2.747	3.453	4.031	5.093

A graph was drawn and is shown below.

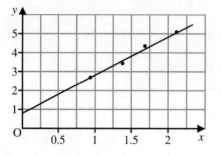

(a) Find the equation of the line in the form $Y = mX + c$ (3 marks)

(b) Hence find the values of the constants a and b in the
relationship $y = ax^b$.   (4 marks)

Specimen
Course assessment B

PAPER I
Calculators may not be used in this paper.
Answers obtained from scale drawings receive no credit.

1 (a) Show that $x = 4$ is a root of the equation
$2x^3 + 15x^2 - 104x + 48 = 0$. (1 mark)
(b) Hence find the other roots. (3 marks)

2 P and Q are the points $(-4, 5)$ and $(2, 7)$.
Find the equation of:
(a) the line PQ (2 marks)
(b) the perpendicular bisector of PQ. (3 marks)

3 The line FG has equation $y = 3x - 1$.
(a) Find, without using calculus, the area of the shaded trapezium shown in the diagram. (2 marks)
(b) Express the area of the trapezium as a definite integral. (1 mark)
(c) Evaluate this integral. (2 marks)

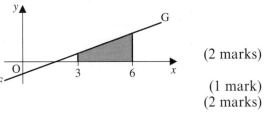

4 The point $A(-3, 9)$ lies on the curve with equation
$y = 3x^2 + 2x - 12$.
Find the equation of the tangent to the curve at A. (4 marks)

5 Part of the graph of $y = f(x)$ is shown in the diagram.

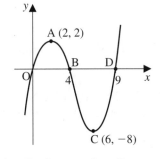

On separate diagrams, sketch the graphs of
(a) $y = f(x - 2)$ (2 marks)
(b) $y = 2 - f(x)$. (3 marks)
Indicate on each graph the images of O, A, B, C and D.

6 The graph of $y = f(x)$ passes through the point $(-1, 2)$.
If $\dfrac{dy}{dx} = x^3 + \dfrac{2}{x^2} - \dfrac{1}{3}$, express y in terms of x. (4 marks)

7 Using triangle ABC, as shown, find the exact value of $\sin 2x$.

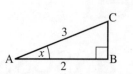

(3 marks)

8 The diagram shows part of the graph of $y = p\cos 4x$ and the line $y = \frac{p}{2}$.

Find the x-coordinates of M and N.

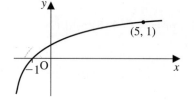

(4 marks)

9 The diagram shows part of the graph of $y = \log_b (x + a)$.
Determine the values of a and b.

(3 marks)

10 A curve has equation $y = x^3(4 - x)$.
Find its stationary values and determine the nature of each. (6 marks)

11 Find $\displaystyle\int \frac{x^2 + 3}{x\sqrt{x}}\, dx$. (4 marks)

12 Two sequences are defined by $u_{n+1} = 0.1u_n + p$, $u_0 = 1$, and $v_{n+1} = 0.7v_n + q$, $v_0 = 1$.
If both sequences have the same limit, express p in terms of q. (3 marks)

PAPER II
Calculators may be used in this paper.
Answers obtained from scale drawings receive no credit.

1 In triangle LMN the coordinates are L(0, 4), M(−2, −6) and N(6, −2).
  (a) Find the equation of the altitude from L to MN. (3 marks)
  (b) Find the equation of the perpendicular bisector of LN. (3 marks)
  (c) Find the coordinates of the point of intersection of these two lines. (2 marks)

2 The diagram shows the circle, centre C, with equation $x^2 + y^2 - 8x - 4y - 20 = 0$.
  (a) Find the equation of the tangent to the circle at the point P(−2, 4). (3 marks)
  (b) The tangent crosses the y-axis at Q. Find the coordinates of Q. (1 mark)
  (c) Another circle centre C is drawn passing through Q. Find the equation of this circle and the point R where PQ meets it again. (4 marks)

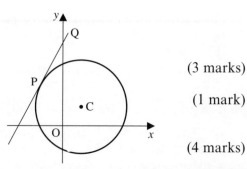

3 Triangle PQR has vertices P(1, 6, 4), Q(4, 3, 1) and R(6, 5, −1).
RQ is extended to S such that $QS = \frac{1}{2}RQ$.
  (a) Find the coordinates of S.   (2 marks)
  (b) Use the scalar product to show that PS is an altitude of
       triangle PQR.   (3 marks)

4 The parabola shown in the diagram has equation
$y = 7 - 6x - x^2$. It intersects the x-axis
at $x = 1$ and A. 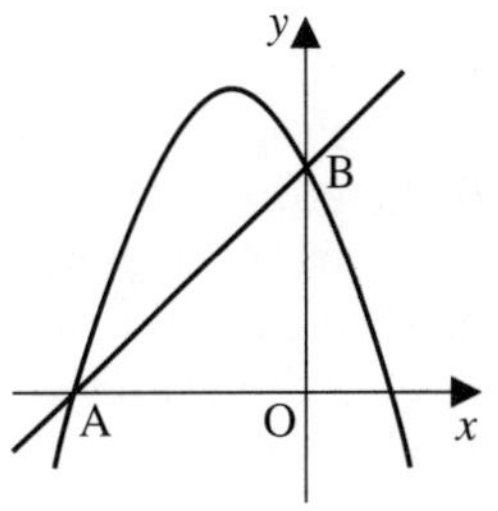
  (a) Find the coordinates of A.   (2 marks)
  (b) B is the point (0, 7).
       Find the equation of AB.   (2 marks)
  (c) Find the area enclosed by the parabola
       and the line AB.   (3 marks)

5 An antibiotic administered to a patient is dissipated by the body
at the rate of 15% per hour.
  (a) If 40 units are administered at 2 pm, how many units remain
       in the patient's body at 5 pm?   (2 marks)
  (b) A course of treatment is suggested which involves
       administering 40 units every 3 hours over a long period of
       time. More than 100 units in the body is considered
       dangerous.
       Is this treatment safe?   (3 marks)

6 Functions f and g are defined on the set of real numbers by

$$f(x) = x^3 + x^2 - 6x$$
$$g(x) = x + 1$$

  (a) Find an expression for f(g(x)).   (2 marks)
  (b) Factorise fully f(g(x)).   (2 marks)

  (c) If $k(x) = \dfrac{1}{f(g(x))}$, for which values of x is k(x) not defined?   (2 marks)

7 In the diagram AB is a diameter of the circle
centre O and radius r units. D is the foot
of the perpendicular from B to OS.
Angle BOS $= \theta°$. 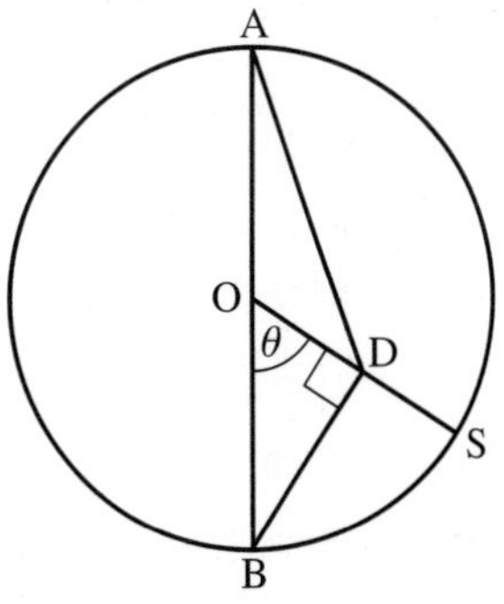
  (a) By applying the cosine rule to triangle AOD,
       or otherwise, prove that $AD^2 = r^2(1 + 3\cos^2 \theta°)$.   (4 marks)
  (b) For the case in which BD bisects angle OBS,

       show that $AD = \dfrac{r}{2}\sqrt{7}$.   [Higher]   (2 marks)

8 In a radioactive substance, the mass m grams at time t years is
given by $m = m_0 e^{-0.03t}$, where m_0 is the original mass.
  (a) If the original mass is 400 grams, what is the mass after 5
       years?   (2 marks)
  (b) How long does it take for the substance to decay to half its
       original mass?   (3 marks)

9 (a) Express $24 \cos x° - 7 \sin x°$ in the form $k \sin(x - \alpha)°$, where
$k > 0$ and $0 \leqslant \alpha \leqslant 360$.   (3 marks)
  (b) Hence solve $24 \cos x° - 7 \sin x° = 20$ for $0 \leqslant x \leqslant 360$.   (4 marks)

10 (a) The point A$(-1, -6)$ lies on the
parabola $y = x^2 + px + q$.
Find a relationship between p and q.   (1 mark)

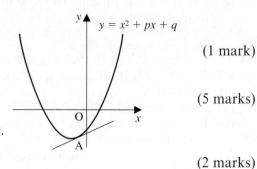

  (b) The tangent to the parabola at A is the
line $y = x - 5$. Find the value of p.
Hence find the equation of the parabola.   (5 marks)
  (c) Using your answers for p and q, find the
value of the discriminant of $x^2 + px + q = 0$.
What feature of the graph is confirmed
by this value?   (2 marks)

11 The cost of laying and operating an oil pipeline over a fixed

distance is given by the formula $C = 250r + \dfrac{27}{r^2}$, where C is the

cost in millions of dollars and r is the radius, in metres, of the
pipe. Calculate the minimum cost of laying and operating the
pipe, and the radius of the pipe which generates this cost.   (5 marks)

Answers to revision exercises

Revision exercise 1

1 (a) $\frac{3}{2}$ **(b)** $-\frac{1}{7}$

2 (a) (i) $m_{PQ} = \frac{2}{9}$, $m_{QR} = -4$, $m_{RS} = \frac{2}{9}$, $m_{PS} = -4$
    (b) Parallelogram

3 (a) $45°$ **(b)** $35.5°$ **(c)** $98.7°$ **(d)** $159°$

4 (a) 0.6 **(b)** -2.05

5 $56.3°$

6 (a) (i) 2 **(ii)** $-\frac{1}{2}$ **(b) (i)** $-\frac{1}{2}$ **(ii)** 2

    (c) (i) -1 **(ii)** 1 **(d) (i)** $-\frac{1}{4}$ **(ii)** 4

    (e) (i) $\frac{5}{2}$ **(ii)** $-\frac{2}{5}$ **(f) (i)** $\frac{3}{4}$ **(ii)** $-\frac{4}{3}$

7 (a) $y = 3x - 5$ **(b)** $y = 6 - 4x$ **(c)** $x + 4y + 16 = 0$

8 (a) $y = 4x - 23$ **(b)** $x - y + 11 = 0$ **(c)** $y = \frac{1}{3}x$

10 (a) $y = 3x + 3$ **(b)** $x + 2y + 7 = 0$

11 (a) $x + y = 2$ **(b)** $x + 5y = 4$

12 Equation of altitude from K is $x = 7$
    Equation of altitude from L is $2x + y = 14$
    Equation of altitude from M is $x + 6y = 7$

13 (a) $y = 3x - 5$ **(b)** $3x + 4y = 6$

14 (a) $10x + y = 26$, $5x - 7y = 18$, $5x + 8y = 8$

15 (a) $3x - y = 1$, $x + 3y = 7$ **(b)** $(1, 2)$

16 $(4, -2)$

17 (a) $4x + y + 2 = 0$ **(b)** $7x - 6y + 11 = 0$ **(c)** $-\frac{23}{31}$

18 (b) (i) Equation of AD is $x - 3y = 6$
          Equation of BE is $4x + 3y + 1 = 0$
    (ii) $\left(1, \ -\frac{5}{3}\right)$

Revision exercise 2

1 (a) $y = 10^x$ **(b)**

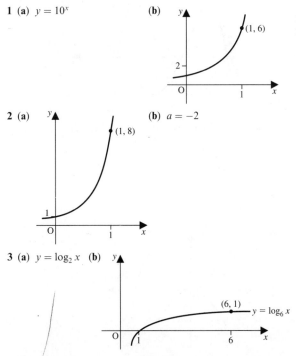

2 (a)   **(b)** $a = -2$

3 (a) $y = \log_2 x$ **(b)**

4

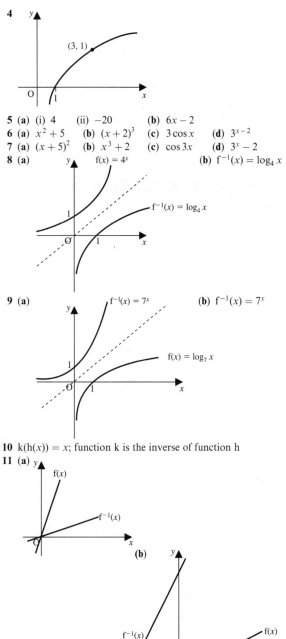

5 (a) (i) 4 **(ii)** -20 **(b)** $6x - 2$

6 (a) $x^2 + 5$ **(b)** $(x + 2)^3$ **(c)** $3\cos x$ **(d)** 3^{x-2}

7 (a) $(x + 5)^2$ **(b)** $x^3 + 2$ **(c)** $\cos 3x$ **(d)** $3^x - 2$

8 (a)   **(b)** $f^{-1}(x) = \log_4 x$

9 (a)   **(b)** $f^{-1}(x) = 7^x$

10 $k(h(x)) = x$; function k is the inverse of function h

11 (a)   **(b)**

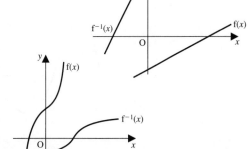

    (c)

12 (a) $\dfrac{1}{x^2 - 6x - 7}$ (b) The set of real numbers, $x \neq -1, 7$

13 (a) $x^4 + 4x^2 + 3$ (b) $(x^2 + 1)(x^2 + 3)$

14 (a) (i) $x^2 - 1$ (ii) $(x - 1)^2$

(b)

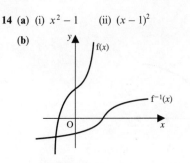

5 (a)

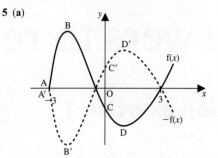

(b) $A'(-3, 0)$, $B'(-2, -3)$, $C'(0, 1)$, $D'(1, 2)$

Revision exercise 3

1 $k = 3$, $n = -2$

2 (a)

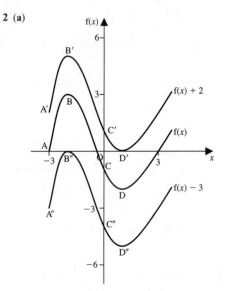

(b) $A'(-3, 2)$, $B'(-2, 5)$, $C'(0, 1)$, $D'(1, 0)$
    $A''(-3, -3)$, $B''(-2, 0)$, $C''(0, -4)$, $D''(1, -5)$

3 $k = 10$, $n = -8$

4 (a)

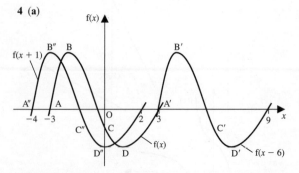

(b) $A'(3, 0)$, $B'(4, 3)$, $C'(6, -1)$, $D'(7, -2)$
    $A''(-4, 0)$, $B''(-3, 3)$, $C''(-1, -1)$, $D''(0, -2)$

6

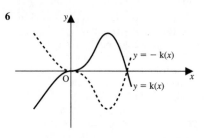

7 (a)

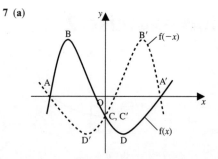

(b) $A'(3, 0)$, $B'(2, 3)$, $C'(0, -1)$, $D'(-1, -2)$

8

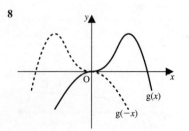

9

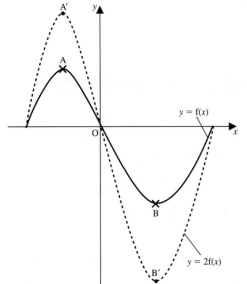

Assuming A$(-2, 3)$ and B$(3, -4)$, A$'$ is $(-2, 6)$ and B$'$ is $(3, -8)$

10

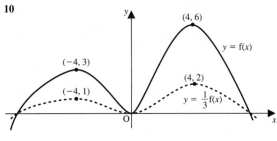

11

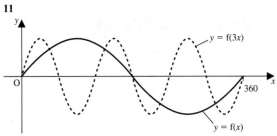

12

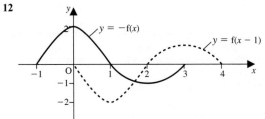

13 (a) $f(x) = x^2 + 2$
(b) $(-2, -2)$

14 (a)

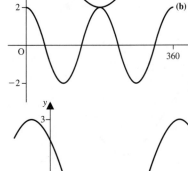

(b) (i) $(-2, 4)$ (ii) $(0, 0)$, $(-4, 0)$
(c) $g(x) = -x(x + 4)$

15 $a = 6$, $b = 4$

16

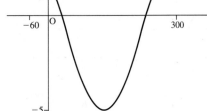

Revision exercise 4

1 (a) $y = -\sin x°$ (b) $y = \sin(x - 45)°$
2 (a) $y = \cos 3x°$ (b) $y = \cos x° - 1$
3

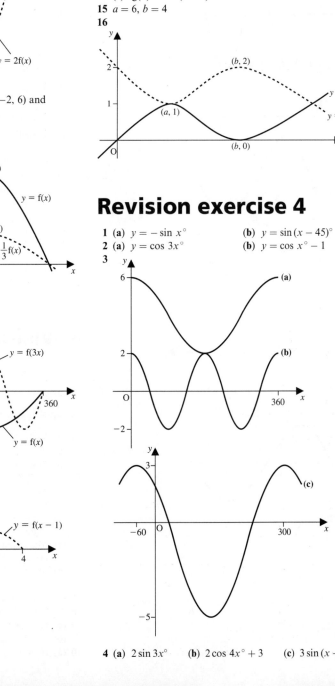

4 (a) $2\sin 3x°$ (b) $2\cos 4x° + 3$ (c) $3\sin(x - 60)°$

5 (a)

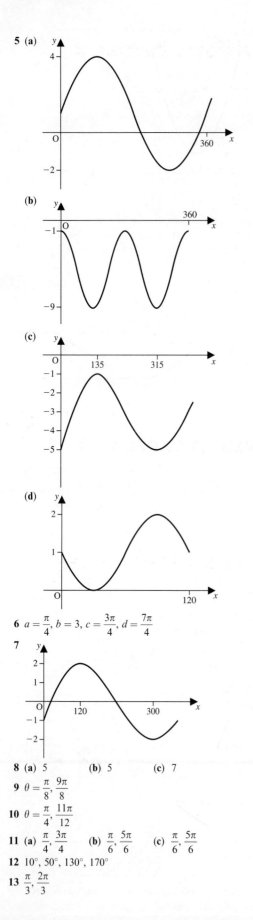

6 $a = \dfrac{\pi}{4}, b = 3, c = \dfrac{3\pi}{4}, d = \dfrac{7\pi}{4}$

7

8 (a) 5   **(b)** 5   **(c)** 7

9 $\theta = \dfrac{\pi}{8}, \dfrac{9\pi}{8}$

10 $\theta = \dfrac{\pi}{4}, \dfrac{11\pi}{12}$

11 (a) $\dfrac{\pi}{4}, \dfrac{3\pi}{4}$ **(b)** $\dfrac{\pi}{6}, \dfrac{5\pi}{6}$ **(c)** $\dfrac{\pi}{6}, \dfrac{5\pi}{6}$

12 $10°, 50°, 130°, 170°$

13 $\dfrac{\pi}{3}, \dfrac{2\pi}{3}$

14 $-6\cos^2 a - \cos a + 1$
$70.529°, 289.471°, 120°, 140°$

15 (a) Before 7 am   **(b)** After 11 am

Revision exercise 5

1 (a) 4.9, 4.99, 4.999, 4.9999; $L = 5$
  (b) 2, −7, −11.5, −13.75; $L = -16$
  (c) 103, 254.5, 481.75, 822.625; no limit
  (d) 8.4, 8.32, 8.336, 8.3328; $L = \dfrac{25}{3}$

2 (a) $A_{n+1} = 0.75A_n + 5, A_0 = 30$
  (b) $L = 20$. Area of algae converges to $20\,\text{m}^2$.

3 (a) $u_{n+1} = 0.5\,u_n + 200, u_0 = 600$
  (b) $L = 400$. Number of aphids converges to 400.

4 (a) $u_{n+1} = 1.03\,u_n + 20, u_0 = 25$
  (b) £135.16

5 (a) 15.775   **(b)** 4   **(c)** $L = 20$

6 (a) $a = 0.3$, i.e. $-1 < a < 1$
  (b) $L = \dfrac{50}{7}$

7 $u_{n+1} = 0.6\,u_n + 150, L = \dfrac{150}{1 - 0.6} = 375$. Since $375 < 500$
stocks will not be kept at an acceptable level.

8 $u_{n+1} = 0.75u_n + 45, u_0 = 45, L = \dfrac{45}{1 - 0.75} = 180$ units

9 (a) £1530.29   **(b)** 1st September
  (c) $u_{n+1} = 1.005\,u_n + 200$, where u_n is the balance on the
    nth month after January.

10 Killpest $L = 769.23$, Pestkill $L = 764.71$, therefore Pestkill
will be more effective

11 Firm A $L = 26.32$, Firm B $L = 23.53$, therefore Firm B
should be employed

12 $a = 0.5, b = 8$

13 Interest rate $= 5\%$, £100 invested each year

Revision exercise 6

1 (a) $3x^2 + 4x$ **(b)** $3x^2 + \dfrac{2}{x^3}$ **(c)** $\dfrac{12}{x^5} - \dfrac{2}{x^3}$

2 (a) $26\frac{1}{2}$ **(b)** $-\frac{3}{2}$

3 (a) $\dfrac{\sqrt{x}}{2}(5x - 3)$ **(b)** $\dfrac{3}{\sqrt{x}} - 1$ **(c)** $1 + \dfrac{1}{x^2} - \dfrac{2}{x^3}$

4 (a) 3   **(b)** −1   **(c)** 7

5 (a) $(0, -2), (3, 25)$
  (b) Point of inflexion $(0, -2)$, maximum turning point
    $(3, 25)$

6 (a) Maximum turning point $\left(-\frac{3}{4}, 2\frac{1}{16}\right)$, minimum turning
    point $\left(\frac{1}{2}, -5\frac{3}{4}\right)$
  (b) Maximum turning point $\left(-\frac{1}{3}, 3\frac{2}{9}\right)$, minimum turning
    point $\left(\frac{1}{2}, -\frac{1}{4}\right)$
  (c) Maximum turning point $(1, 7)$, minimum turning
    point $(2, 5)$
  (d) Maximum turning point $(0, 6)$, minimum turning
    point $\left(\frac{1}{3}, 5\frac{23}{27}\right)$

7 (a) $y - 4x + 4 = 0$ **(b)** $y = x + 2$

8 $4y - 8x - 7 = 0$

9 (a) $(1, -1), (-3, 23)$
  (b) $y = 2x - 3, y = 2x + 29$

10 (a) $(6, 41)$ **(b)** $\left(\frac{3}{2}, 7\frac{1}{4}\right)$

11 (a)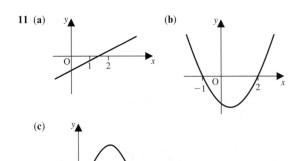

(b)

(c)

12 (b) $\dfrac{10}{\sqrt{3}}$

13 0

Revision exercise 7

1 $(x+3)(2x+1)(x-1)$
2 (a) $(x-1)(x-3)(x-4)$ **(b)** $(x+1)(2x-1)(x+3)$
4 $0, 1, -1$
5 (a) $(x^2+7x+32), 164$ **(b)** $(3x^2-16x+53), -155$
6 $-32, (x+3)(2x+1)(x-5)$
7 $-34, (2x-1)(2x-3)(2x+5)$
8 (a) $c=-13$, other zeros are $-\frac{1}{2}, -2$
   (b) $c=-1$, other zeros are $\frac{1}{3}, 2$
9 $a=-8, b=1$
10 $a:b=2:1$
12 $y=3x^3-3x^2-12x+12$
13 $y=\dfrac{-x^3}{2}-2x^2+\dfrac{x}{2}+2$
14 $y=\dfrac{x^3}{3}+\dfrac{7x^2}{3}+\dfrac{7x}{3}-5$
15

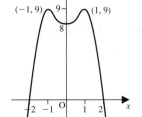

16 (a)

(b) $x\neq-1, x<1$

17 (b) 2.09
18 1.80
19 0.2

Revision exercise 8

1 (a) Roots are non-real
   (b) Roots are real and unequal
   (c) Roots are real and equal
2 (a) $b^2-4ac=4>0$, therefore two real roots
   (b) $b^2-4ac=0$, therefore one real root
   (c) $b^2-4ac=-4<0$, therefore there are no real roots
3 (a) $y=4x^2-16x+12$
   (b) $y=-2x^2+4x+6$
   (c) $y=x^2+10x+27$
4 (a) $-3<x<\frac{1}{2}$
   (b) $x<-1, x>\frac{3}{2}$
   (c) $x<-5, x>\frac{3}{2}$
5 (a) $p=\pm4$ **(b)** $p=0$ or $\frac{4}{3}$
6 (a) $k<-6\frac{1}{4}$ **(b)** $k<-4, k>4$
7 $k<2$
8 $k=\dfrac{-10}{9}$ or 2
9 (a) Discriminant $=k^2+4$, which must always be >0, therefore roots are always real
   (b) Discriminant $=(k-2)^2$, which must always be $\geqslant0$, therefore roots are always real
10 Discriminant $=4(k-2)(k+3)$, therefore k cannot have a value between -3 and 2 for $4(k-2)(k+3)>0$
11 (a) Discriminant $=p^2+4q^2$, which must always be $\geqslant0$, therefore roots are always real
   (b) Discriminant $=(p+q)^2$, which must always be $\geqslant0$, therefore roots are always real
   (c) Discriminant $=(p-2q)^2$, which must always be $\geqslant0$, therefore roots are always real
12 $k=4$
13 $x=1, y=0$
14 $b^2-4ac=0$, therefore the line is a tangent
15 $m=\pm2$
16 $y=2x+1$

Revision exercise 9

1 (a) $\dfrac{x^4}{4}+2\sqrt{x}+c$ **(b)** $3x^3+15x^2+25x+c$
   (c) $\frac{2}{7}x^{\frac{7}{2}}-\frac{10}{3}x^{\frac{3}{2}}+c$
2 (a) $\frac{1}{2}$ **(b)** $12\frac{1}{6}$ **(c)** $-5\frac{1}{3}$
3 (a) 22   **(b)** $52\frac{1}{12}$ **(c)** 36
4 (a) $\displaystyle\int_0^3 3x-x^2\,dx$ **(b)** $\displaystyle\int_0^{\sqrt{2}} 2x-x^3\,dx$
   (c) $\displaystyle\int_1^3 8x-2x^2-6\,dx$
5 (a) (i) 30 **(ii)**

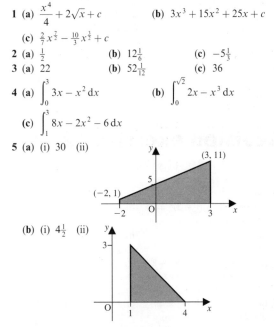

(b) (i) $4\frac{1}{2}$ **(ii)**

(c) (i) 11 (ii)

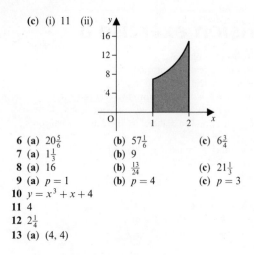

6 (a) $20\frac{5}{6}$ **(b)** $57\frac{1}{6}$ **(c)** $6\frac{3}{4}$
7 (a) $1\frac{1}{3}$ **(b)** 9
8 (a) 16 **(b)** $\frac{13}{24}$ **(c)** $21\frac{1}{3}$
9 (a) $p = 1$ **(b)** $p = 4$ **(c)** $p = 3$
10 $y = x^3 + x + 4$
11 4
12 $2\frac{1}{4}$
13 (a) (4, 4)

Revision exercise 11

1 (a) $48.2°, 311.8°$ **(b)** $30°, 150°, 270°$
  (c) $45°, 135°, 225°, 315°$ **(d)** $11.8°, 108.2°$
2 (a) $\dfrac{\pi}{12}, \dfrac{11\pi}{12}, \dfrac{13\pi}{12}, \dfrac{23\pi}{12}$ **(b)** $\dfrac{\pi}{6}, \dfrac{5\pi}{6}, \dfrac{7\pi}{6}, \dfrac{11\pi}{6}$
  (c) $\dfrac{\pi}{2}, \pi, \dfrac{3\pi}{2}$ **(d)** $\dfrac{\pi}{3}, \dfrac{4\pi}{3}$
3 (a) $\dfrac{56}{65}$ **(b)** $\dfrac{204}{325}$
4 (a) $\sin(x - 60)°$ **(b)** $90°$
5 (a) $\cos\left(x - \dfrac{\pi}{4}\right)$ **(b)** $\pi, \dfrac{3\pi}{2}$
7 (a) $\cos 75° = \cos(45 + 30)° = \dfrac{\sqrt{3} - 1}{2\sqrt{2}}$
  (b) $\sin 105° = \sin(60 + 45)° = \dfrac{\sqrt{3} + 1}{2\sqrt{2}}$
8 (a) $\dfrac{1}{\sqrt{2}}$ **(b)** $\dfrac{\sqrt{3}}{2}$ **(c)** $\dfrac{\sqrt{3}}{2}$ **(d)** 1 **(e)** $\dfrac{\sqrt{3} - \sqrt{2} - 1}{\sqrt{2}}$
  (f) $\frac{1}{4}$
12 (a) $0, \dfrac{\pi}{3}, \pi, \dfrac{5\pi}{3}, 2\pi$ **(b)** $\dfrac{\pi}{6}, \dfrac{5\pi}{6}, \dfrac{3\pi}{2}$
  (c) $\dfrac{\pi}{6}, \dfrac{5\pi}{6}, \dfrac{7\pi}{6}, \dfrac{11\pi}{6}$ **(d)** π
13 $210°$
14 $\dfrac{3\sqrt{7}}{8}$
15 $164.8°$

Revision exercise 12

1 (a) $x^2 + y^2 = 64$ **(b)** $x^2 + y^2 = 169$ **(c)** $x^2 + y^2 = p^2$
2 $x^2 + y^2 = 28$
3 (a) $(4, -9), 7$ **(b)** $(0, -11), 2\sqrt{11}$
4 (a) $(x - 2)^2 + (y - 3)^2 = 25$ **(b)** $(x + 7)^2 + (y - 1)^2 = 63$
  (c) $(x - t)^2 + (y - u)^2 = a^2$
5 (a) $(-4, -1), 4$ **(b)** $(6, -4), 8$
  (c) $(1, 3), \sqrt{7}$ **(d)** $(7, 0), 7$
6 (a) $x^2 + y^2 + 2x - 8y - 8 = 0$
  (b) $x^2 + y^2 - 6x + 6y - 63 = 0$
  (c) $x^2 + y^2 - 4x + 3 = 0$
7 (a) $(3, 3)$ **(b)** $(-3, 2)$ **(c)** $(1, -5)$ **(d)** $(2, 1)$
8 $y + 2x = 7$

9 (a) $2x + y = 15$ **(b)** $3x - y + 5 = 0$
  (c) $4x + 3y + 9 = 0$
10 4
11 $(x - 6)^2 + (y - 6)^2 = 36, (x - 6)^2 + (y + 3)^2 = 9$
12 5
13 $y = 2x + 2, y = -5.5x + 2$
14 (a) **(i)** $78.26\,\mathrm{cm}$ **(ii)** $133\,\mathrm{mm}$
  (b) **(i)** 1 **(ii)** $x + y = 10$, (8, 2) and (6, 4)

Revision exercise 13

1 (a) $\overrightarrow{AB} = \begin{pmatrix} -6 \\ 6 \end{pmatrix}, |\overrightarrow{AB}| = 6\sqrt{2}$ **(b)** $(1, -2)$
  (c) $(0, -1)$
2 (a) $\overrightarrow{PQ} = \begin{pmatrix} 1 \\ 5 \\ -2 \end{pmatrix}$
4 $(-1, 2, 11)$
5 $(0, -2, -4)$
6 (a) -9 **(b)** $136.1°$
7 $69.8°$
8 $\begin{pmatrix} -5 \\ -5 \\ 7 \end{pmatrix}$
9 (a) $60°$ **(b)** **(i)** $4\frac{1}{2}$ **(ii)** 9
10 $(-1, 6, -23)$
11 $47.05°$
13 (a) **(iv)** Square **(b)** $\dfrac{k}{2}\tan\theta$
14 (b) $(4, 6, 4)$ **(c)** $(4\frac{2}{3}, 6\frac{2}{3}, 2\frac{2}{3})$
15 (a) $\begin{pmatrix} -9 \\ 12 \\ 3 \end{pmatrix}$ **(b)** $(-1, 2, 6)$
16 (a) C divides AB in the ratio 5:3
17 (a) $\begin{pmatrix} -8 \\ 18 \\ 4 \end{pmatrix}$ **(b)** $\begin{pmatrix} 1 \\ 10 \\ 9\frac{1}{2} \end{pmatrix}$ **(c)** $40.9°$
18 (a) **(i)** 4 **(ii)** 9 **(iii)** 3 **(b)** $v.v = 108, 6\sqrt{3}$

Revision exercise 14

1 (a) $5\cos x$ **(b)** $3\sin x$
  (c) $-\frac{2}{3}\sin x - 2\cos x$ **(d)** $-3\sin x - \frac{2}{5}\cos x$
  (e) $-\frac{1}{2}\sin x$ **(f)** $-\frac{1}{5}\cos x$
2 (a) $3\sin x + C$ **(b)** $2\cos\theta + C$ **(c)** $-\frac{2}{7}\cos t + C$
3 (a) $8x(x^2 - 3)^3$ **(b)** $5(9x^2 - 4x)(3x^3 - 2x^2 + 1)^4$
  (c) $10(x - 2)^9$ **(d)** $4\cos 4x$
  (e) $-4\sin 4x - 6\cos 2x$ **(f)** $2\cos(3 - 2x)$
  (g) $\dfrac{-40x}{(x^2 + 3)^5}$ **(h)** $\dfrac{-6x^3}{\sqrt{5 - 3x^4}}$ **(i)** $-4\sin x\cos^3 x$
  (j) $\dfrac{\cos x}{2\sqrt{\sin x}}$ **(k)** $2\sin x\cos x$ **(l)** $\dfrac{-1}{\sqrt{(2x - 1)^3}}$
4 (a) $5424\frac{1}{7}$ **(b)** 260 **(c)** 1.5
5 (a) $y = 216x - 351$ **(b)** $y = -2\theta + \pi$
6 (a) Minimum turning point $(0, -64)$, points of inflexion $(2, 0)$ and $(-2, 0)$
  (b) Minimum turning points $(0, 0)$, $(\pi, 0)$ and $(2\pi, 0)$
    Maximum turning points $\left(\dfrac{\pi}{2}, 1\right)$ and $\left(\dfrac{3\pi}{2}, 1\right)$

7 18

8 (a) 5.84   **(b)** $2\frac{1}{32}$

   (c) $\frac{4}{3}$ **(d)** $21\frac{1}{4}$

9 (a) 2.5   **(b)** 12.35

10 $f(x) = \dfrac{(5x-3)^6}{30} + 29\frac{13}{15}$

11 £384 000, $\sqrt{60}$

Revision exercise 15

1 (a) 4   **(b)** 3   **(c)** 6

2 (a) 5   **(b)** $\log_a 9$ **(c)** 6   **(d)** 1

   (e) 4   **(f)** $\frac{1}{2}$ **(g)** $10\log_5 3$ **(h)** -2

3 (a) $\log_3 7$ **(b)** $\log_2 11$ **(c)** $\log_5 \frac{1}{10}$

4 (a) 1.099   **(b)** 1.609   **(c)** 1.292

5 (a) $8^{2.8}$ **(b)** $7^{0.8}$ **(c)** $3^{-0.5}$

6 (a) 29.36   **(b)** 13.04   **(c)** 0.22

7 (a) 126   **(b)** 2

8 (a) 20   **(b)** 0.693

9 -0.2

10 (a) 20   **(b)** 0.916 hours

11 (a) 0.026   **(b)** 26.65 minutes

12 $a = 1.8$, $b = 1.5$

13 (a) $y = 1000\sqrt{x}$ **(b)** $y = 31.6x^{-2}$

14 (a) $y = 100(1.26)^x$ **(b)** $y = 10000(0.02)^x$

15 $A\left(\frac{1}{4}, 0\right)$, $B(2, 9)$

16 $a = 3$, $b = 2$

17 $a = 4$, $b = 5$

Revision exercise 16

1 (a) $\sqrt{2}\cos(x - 45)°$ **(b)** $5\cos(x - 323.1)°$

2 (a) $2\cos(x + 330)°$ **(b)** $\sqrt{13}\cos(x + 236.3)°$

3 (a) $5.59\sin(x - 296.6)°$ **(b)** $\sqrt{8}\sin(x - 240)°$

4 (a) $\sqrt{29}\sin(x + 111.8)°$ **(b)** $\sqrt{89}\sin(x + 328)°$

5 (a) $3\sqrt{2}\cos\left(\theta - \dfrac{3\pi}{4}\right)$ **(b)** $4\cos\left(\theta - \dfrac{5\pi}{3}\right)$

6 (a) $2\sin\left(\theta + \dfrac{2\pi}{3}\right)$ **(b)** $2\sqrt{2}\sin\left(\theta + \dfrac{5\pi}{4}\right)$

7 $5\sin(2x - 233.1)°$

8 $\sqrt{26}\sin(8\theta + 0.437\pi)$

9 (a) $5\sqrt{5}\cos(x - 26.6)°$ minimum value $= 5\sqrt{5}$

   (b) $\sqrt{41}\cos(x - 128.7)°$ minimum value $= \sqrt{41}$

10 (a) $2\cos\left(\theta - \dfrac{5\pi}{6}\right)$ maximum value $= -2$

   (b) $2\sqrt{41}\cos(\theta - 1.785\pi)$ maximum value $= -2\sqrt{41}$

11 (a) $25\sqrt{2}\sin\left(\omega t + \dfrac{\pi}{4}\right)$ **(b)** 135.36

12 (a) $\sqrt{13}\cos(x - 56.3)$ **(b)** $138.3°$, $334.3°$

13 (a) $107.6°$, $319.8°$ **(b)** $36.9°$

14 $\dfrac{\pi}{3}$, π

15 (a) $2\cos(20t - 60)$ **(b)**

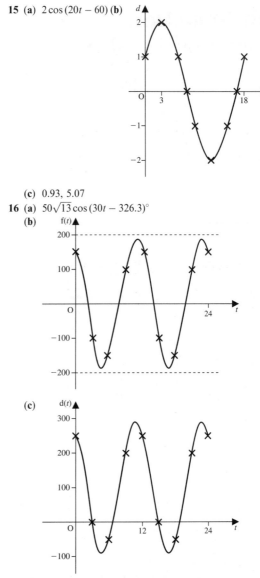

   (c) 0.93, 5.07

16 (a) $50\sqrt{13}\cos(30t - 326.3)°$

   (b)

   (c)

   (d) 4 hours 52.8 minutes

   (e) Must avoid entering harbour between 0.45 and 9.00 and 12.45 and 21.00

17 (a) $2500 + 400\sin(120t + 120)°$

   (b)

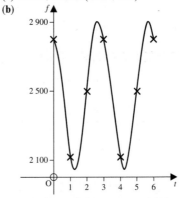

   (c) Alarm sounds from start to 0.095 seconds, then from 2.405 to 3.095 seconds, then from 5.405 to 6.095 seconds

Specimen Unit assessment A–1(H)

1 $m = \dfrac{2-(-1)}{-2-4} = -\dfrac{1}{2}$

$y + 1 = -\dfrac{1}{2}(x - 4)$

$2y + 2 = -x + 4$

$x + 2y = 2$

2 $m = \tan 70° = 2.75$

3 (a) $m = 3$

(b) $m = -\dfrac{1}{3}$

4 (a)

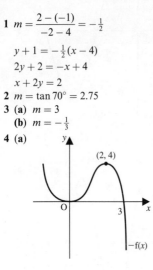

(b)

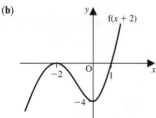

5 (a) $y = \sin x - 2$

(b) $y = \dfrac{1}{2}\cos x$

6 Substitute $(2, 4)$ in $y = a^x$

$4 = a^2$

$a = 2$, therefore $y = 2^x$

7 $y = \log_5 x$

8 (a) $f(g(x)) = f(3x + 1) = (3x + 1)^2$

$= 9x^2 + 6x + 1$

(b) $k(h(x)) = k(2x) = \sin 2x$

9 $y = \dfrac{x^4 - 1}{x^2} = x^2 - \dfrac{1}{x^2} = x^2 - x^{-2}$

$\dfrac{dy}{dx} = 2x + 2x^{-3} = 2x + \dfrac{2}{x^3}$

10 $y = x^2 - 10x + 24$

$\dfrac{dy}{dx} = 2x - 10$

At $x = 7$, $m = 14 - 10 = 4$

11 $y = \dfrac{1}{3}x^3 + 2x^2 + 3x + 4$

$\dfrac{dy}{dx} = x^2 + 4x + 3$

$= (x + 3)(x + 1) = 0$ for stationary points

$x = -3 \quad x = -1$

when $x = -3$, $y = -9 + 18 - 9 + 4 = 4$, $(-3, 4)$

when $x = -1$, $y = -\dfrac{1}{3} + 2 - 3 + 4 = 2\dfrac{2}{3}$, $(-1, 2\dfrac{2}{3})$

x	-3^-	-3	-3^+
$\dfrac{dy}{dx}$	$+$	0	$-$
slope	/	—	\

maximum turning point at $(-3, 4)$

x	-1^-	-1	-1^+
$\dfrac{dy}{dx}$	$-$	0	$+$
slope	\	—	/

minimum turning point at $(-1, 2\dfrac{2}{3})$

12 (a) $u_{n+1} = \dfrac{4}{5} u_n + 2000$

(b) Since $-1 < a < 1$, limit L exists

$L = \dfrac{b}{1 - a} = \dfrac{2000}{1 - \dfrac{4}{5}} = 10{,}000$

The number of tadpoles will never exceed 10,000

Specimen Unit assessment B–1(H)

1 $m = \dfrac{-5 - (-3)}{4 - 2} = -\dfrac{2}{2} = -1$

$y + 3 = -1(x - 2)$

$y + 3 = -x + 2$

$x + y + 1 = 0$

2 $m = \tan 38° = 0.78$

3 (a) $m = \dfrac{1}{2}$ (b) $m = -2$

4 (a) (i)

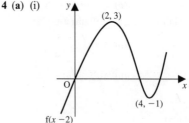

(ii)

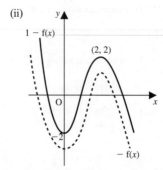

(b) (i) a = 3

(ii)

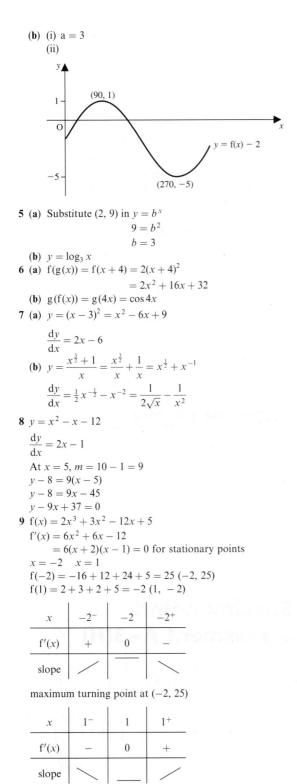

5 (a) Substitute (2, 9) in $y = b^x$
$$9 = b^2$$
$$b = 3$$

(b) $y = \log_3 x$

6 (a) $f(g(x)) = f(x + 4) = 2(x + 4)^2$
$$= 2x^2 + 16x + 32$$

(b) $g(f(x)) = g(4x) = \cos 4x$

7 (a) $y = (x - 3)^2 = x^2 - 6x + 9$
$$\frac{dy}{dx} = 2x - 6$$

(b) $y = \dfrac{x^{\frac{3}{2}} + 1}{x} = \dfrac{x^{\frac{3}{2}}}{x} + \dfrac{1}{x} = x^{\frac{1}{2}} + x^{-1}$
$$\frac{dy}{dx} = \tfrac{1}{2}x^{-\frac{1}{2}} - x^{-2} = \frac{1}{2\sqrt{x}} - \frac{1}{x^2}$$

8 $y = x^2 - x - 12$
$$\frac{dy}{dx} = 2x - 1$$
At $x = 5$, $m = 10 - 1 = 9$
$$y - 8 = 9(x - 5)$$
$$y - 8 = 9x - 45$$
$$y - 9x + 37 = 0$$

9 $f(x) = 2x^3 + 3x^2 - 12x + 5$
$$f'(x) = 6x^2 + 6x - 12$$
$$= 6(x + 2)(x - 1) = 0 \text{ for stationary points}$$
$$x = -2 \quad x = 1$$
$$f(-2) = -16 + 12 + 24 + 5 = 25 \ (-2, 25)$$
$$f(1) = 2 + 3 + 2 + 5 = -2 \ (1, \ -2)$$

x	-2^-	-2	-2^+
$f'(x)$	+	0	−
slope	/	—	\

maximum turning point at (−2, 25)

x	1^-	1	1^+
$f'(x)$	−	0	+
slope	\	—	/

minimum turning point at (1, −2)

10 (a) $u_{n+1} = 0.7 u_n + 100$

(b) Since $-1 < a < 1$, limit L exists
$$L = \frac{b}{1 - a} = \frac{100}{1 - 0.7} = 333\tfrac{1}{3}$$

Eventually the number of aphids will converge to 333

Specimen Unit assessment A–2(H)

1 (a)

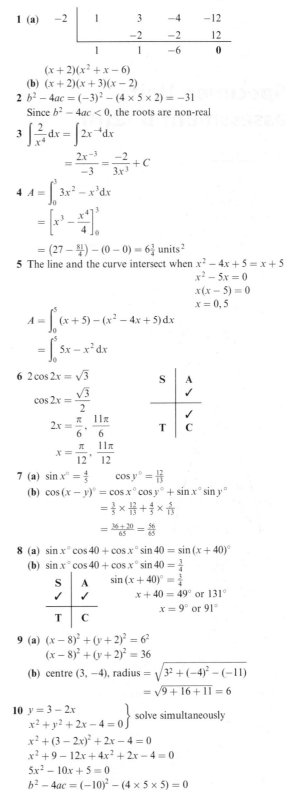

$$-2 \ \begin{array}{|rrrr} 1 & 3 & -4 & -12 \\ & -2 & -2 & 12 \\ \hline 1 & 1 & -6 & 0 \end{array}$$

$(x + 2)(x^2 + x - 6)$

(b) $(x + 2)(x + 3)(x - 2)$

2 $b^2 - 4ac = (-3)^2 - (4 \times 5 \times 2) = -31$
Since $b^2 - 4ac < 0$, the roots are non-real

3 $\displaystyle\int \frac{2}{x^4} dx = \int 2x^{-4} dx$
$$= \frac{2x^{-3}}{-3} = \frac{-2}{3x^3} + C$$

4 $A = \displaystyle\int_0^3 3x^2 - x^3 dx$
$$= \left[x^3 - \frac{x^4}{4} \right]_0^3$$
$$= \left(27 - \tfrac{81}{4} \right) - (0 - 0) = 6\tfrac{3}{4} \text{ units}^2$$

5 The line and the curve intersect when $x^2 - 4x + 5 = x + 5$
$$x^2 - 5x = 0$$
$$x(x - 5) = 0$$
$$x = 0, 5$$
$$A = \int_0^5 (x + 5) - (x^2 - 4x + 5) dx$$
$$= \int_0^5 5x - x^2 dx$$

6 $2\cos 2x = \sqrt{3}$
$$\cos 2x = \frac{\sqrt{3}}{2}$$
$$2x = \frac{\pi}{6}, \frac{11\pi}{6}$$
$$x = \frac{\pi}{12}, \frac{11\pi}{12}$$

S	A
	✓
	✓
T	**C**

7 (a) $\sin x° = \tfrac{4}{5}$ $\qquad \cos y° = \tfrac{12}{13}$

(b) $\cos (x - y)° = \cos x° \cos y° + \sin x° \sin y°$
$$= \tfrac{3}{5} \times \tfrac{12}{13} + \tfrac{4}{5} \times \tfrac{5}{13}$$
$$= \tfrac{36 + 20}{65} = \tfrac{56}{65}$$

8 (a) $\sin x° \cos 40 + \cos x° \sin 40 = \sin (x + 40)°$

(b) $\sin x° \cos 40 + \cos x° \sin 40 = \tfrac{3}{4}$
$$\sin (x + 40)° = \tfrac{3}{4}$$
$$x + 40 = 49° \text{ or } 131°$$
$$x = 9° \text{ or } 91°$$

S	A
✓	✓
T	**C**

9 (a) $(x - 8)^2 + (y + 2)^2 = 6^2$
$$(x - 8)^2 + (y + 2)^2 = 36$$

(b) centre (3, −4), radius $= \sqrt{3^2 + (-4)^2 - (-11)}$
$$= \sqrt{9 + 16 + 11} = 6$$

10 $\left. \begin{array}{l} y = 3 - 2x \\ x^2 + y^2 + 2x - 4 = 0 \end{array} \right\}$ solve simultaneously
$$x^2 + (3 - 2x)^2 + 2x - 4 = 0$$
$$x^2 + 9 - 12x + 4x^2 + 2x - 4 = 0$$
$$5x^2 - 10x + 5 = 0$$
$$b^2 - 4ac = (-10)^2 - (4 \times 5 \times 5) = 0$$
Roots are equal, hence tangency

11 $m_{CP} = \dfrac{-1-(-6)}{4-1} = \frac{5}{3}$

$m_{tan} = -\frac{3}{5}$ P(1, −6)

$y + 6 = -\frac{3}{5}(x - 1)$

$5y + 30 = -3x + 3$

$3x + 5y + 27 = 0$

Specimen Unit assessment B–2(H)

1 (a)

$$
\begin{array}{r|rrrr}
1 & 3 & -7 & -3 & 7 \\
  &   & 3 & -4 & -7 \\
\hline
  & 3 & -4 & -7 & 0
\end{array}
$$

$(x - 1)(3x^2 - 4x - 7)$

(b) $(x - 1)(x + 1)(3x - 7)$

2 $b^2 - 4ac = (-3)^2 - (4 \times 2 \times 7) = -47$

Since $b^2 - 4ac < 0$, the roots are non-real

3 $\displaystyle\int 2x^2 + 4x^{-\frac{1}{2}}\,dx = \dfrac{2x^3}{3} + \dfrac{4x^{\frac{1}{2}}}{\frac{1}{2}} = \dfrac{2x^3}{3} + 8\sqrt{x} + C$

4 $\displaystyle\int \dfrac{x^2}{x^2} + \dfrac{4}{x^2}\,dx = \int 1 + 4x^{-2}\,dx = x + \dfrac{4x^{-1}}{-1} = x - \dfrac{4}{x} + C$

5 $A = \int_{-1}^{2} x^3 - 3x + 4\,dx$

$= \left[\dfrac{x^4}{4} - \dfrac{3x^2}{2} + 4x\right]_{-1}^{2}$

$= (4 - 6 + 8) - (\frac{1}{4} - \frac{3}{2} - 4) = 11\frac{1}{4}$ units^2

6

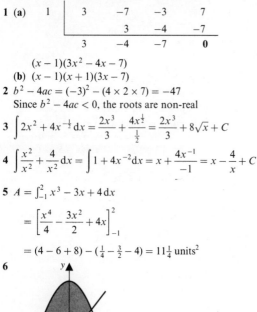

The line and the curve intersect when

$x^2 + 2x - 15 = 0$

$(x + 5)(x - 3) = 0$

$x = -5, 3$

$A = \int_{-5}^{3} (15 - x^2) - 2x\,dx$

$= \left[15x - \dfrac{x^3}{3} - x^2\right]_{-5}^{3}$

$= (45 - 9 - 9) - (-75 + \frac{125}{3} - 25)$

$= 85\frac{1}{3}$ units^2

7 $\cos(\alpha + \beta)^\circ = \cos\alpha^\circ \cos\beta^\circ - \sin\alpha^\circ \sin\beta^\circ$

$= \dfrac{4}{\sqrt{20}} \times \dfrac{\sqrt{20}}{5} - \dfrac{2}{\sqrt{20}} \times \dfrac{\sqrt{5}}{5}$

$= \dfrac{4\sqrt{20} - 2\sqrt{5}}{5\sqrt{20}} = \dfrac{8\sqrt{5} - 2\sqrt{5}}{10\sqrt{5}}$

$= \dfrac{6\sqrt{5}}{10\sqrt{5}} = \dfrac{6}{10} = \dfrac{3}{5}$

8 (a) $\sin x^\circ \cos 10^\circ - \cos x^\circ \sin 10^\circ = \sin(x - 10)^\circ$

(b) $\sin x^\circ \cos 10^\circ - \cos x^\circ \sin 10^\circ = \frac{2}{5}$

S	A
✓	✓
T	C

$\sin(x - 10)^\circ = \frac{2}{5}$

$x - 10 = 24^\circ, 156^\circ$

$x = 34^\circ, 166^\circ$

9

$\cos 2x^\circ - \cos x^\circ = 0$

$(2\cos^2 x^\circ - 1) - \cos x^\circ = 0$

$2\cos^2 x^\circ - \cos x^\circ - 1 = 0$

$(2\cos x^\circ + 1)(\cos x^\circ - 1) = 0$

$\cos x^\circ = -\frac{1}{2} \quad \cos x^\circ = 1$

$x = 120, 240 \quad x = 0, 360$

$\{0, 120, 240, 360\}$

S	A
✓	
✓	
T	C

10 centre $(-2, -3)$, radius $= \sqrt{(-2)^2 + (-3)^2 - (-12)}$

$= \sqrt{4 + 9 + 12} = 5$

11 $(x - (-5))^2 + (y - 2)^2 = 5^2$

$(x + 5)^2 + (y - 2)^2 = 25$

12 $\left.\begin{array}{l} y = 5 + 2x \\ x^2 + y^2 = 5 \end{array}\right\}$ solve simultaneously

$x^2 + (5 + 2x)^2 = 5$

$x^2 + 25 + 20x + 4x^2 - 5 = 0$

$5(x^2 + 4x + 4) = 0$

$b^2 - 4ac = 4^2 - (4 \times 1 \times 4) = 0$

Roots are equal, hence tangency

13 centre C (2, 0), A (3, −2)

$m_{AC} = \dfrac{0 - (-2)}{2 - 3} = -2$

$m_{tan} = \frac{1}{2}$

$y + 2 = \frac{1}{2}(x - 3)$

$2y + 4 = x - 3$

$2y - x + 7 = 0$

Specimen Unit assessment A–3(H)

1 (a) (i) $\overrightarrow{AC} = \mathbf{c} - \mathbf{a} = \begin{pmatrix} 3 \\ -2 \\ 9 \end{pmatrix} - \begin{pmatrix} 1 \\ 2 \\ 3 \end{pmatrix} = \begin{pmatrix} 2 \\ -4 \\ 6 \end{pmatrix}$

(ii) $\overrightarrow{AB} = \mathbf{b} - \mathbf{a} = \begin{pmatrix} 4 \\ -14 \\ 12 \end{pmatrix} - \begin{pmatrix} 1 \\ 2 \\ 3 \end{pmatrix} = \begin{pmatrix} 3 \\ -6 \\ 9 \end{pmatrix}$

$= 1\frac{1}{2}\overrightarrow{AC}$

so $\overrightarrow{AC}$ and $\overrightarrow{AB}$ are parallel and since A is a common point, A, B and C are collinear

(b) $\mathbf{l} = \frac{1}{3}\mathbf{k} + \frac{2}{3}\mathbf{m} = \frac{1}{3}(\mathbf{k} + 2\mathbf{m})$

$= \frac{1}{3}\begin{pmatrix} -1 \\ 0 \\ 3 \end{pmatrix} + \begin{pmatrix} 16 \\ 6 \\ 0 \end{pmatrix} = \frac{1}{3}\begin{pmatrix} 15 \\ 6 \\ 3 \end{pmatrix} = \begin{pmatrix} 5 \\ 2 \\ 1 \end{pmatrix}$

L (5, 2, 1)

2 (a) $\overrightarrow{PQ}.\overrightarrow{PR} = \begin{pmatrix} 2 \\ -1 \\ -2 \end{pmatrix}.\begin{pmatrix} -3 \\ 0 \\ 4 \end{pmatrix} = -6 - 0 - 8 = -14$

(b) $\left|\overrightarrow{PQ}\right| = \sqrt{4+1+4} = 3$

$\left|\overrightarrow{PR}\right| = \sqrt{9+0+16} = 5$

$\cos\theta = \dfrac{\overrightarrow{PQ}.\overrightarrow{PR}}{\left|\overrightarrow{PQ}\right|\left|\overrightarrow{PR}\right|}$

$= \dfrac{-14}{3 \times 5} = \dfrac{-14}{15}$

$\theta = 159°$

S ✓	A
T	C

3 (a) $y = -2\sin x \qquad \dfrac{dy}{dx} = -2\cos x$

(b) $y = \tfrac{1}{3}\cos x \qquad \dfrac{dy}{dx} = -\tfrac{1}{3}\sin x$

4 $f(x) = (4x+3)^3$
$f'(x) = 3(4x+3)^2 \times 4 = 12(4x+3)^2$

5 (a) $\int -2\cos x\,dx = -2\sin x + C$

(b) $\int \tfrac{3}{4}\sin x\,dx = -\tfrac{3}{4}\cos x + C$

(c) $\int_1^3 (x-1)^3\,dx = \left[\dfrac{(x-1)^4}{4}\right]_1^3 = \left(\tfrac{16}{4}\right) - (0) = 4$

6 (a) $\log_a 10 - \log_a 2 = \log_a \tfrac{10}{2} = \log_a 5$

(b) $4\log_8 2 + \log_8 4 = \log_8 2^4 + \log_8 4$
$= \log_8 (16 \times 4) = \log_8 64 = \log_8 8^2$
$= 2\log_8 8 = 2$

7 (a)
$3^x = 8$
$\log 3^x = \log 8$
$x\log 3 = \log 8$
$x = \dfrac{\log 8}{\log 3}$

(b) $x = \dfrac{\log_e 5}{\log_e 2}$
$= \dfrac{0.699}{0.301}$
$= 2.32$

(c) $\log_{10} y = 4.1$
$y = 10^{4.1}$

(d) $y = 10^{1.9}$
$= 79.4$

8 $3\cos x° + 5\sin x° = k\cos(x-a)°$
$= k\cos x° \cos a° + k\sin x° \sin a°$

$\left.\begin{array}{r} 3 = k\cos a° \\ 5 = k\sin a° \end{array}\right\} \quad k = \sqrt{3^2 + 5^2} = \sqrt{34}$

S ✓	A ✓✓
T	C ✓

$\tan a° = \tfrac{5}{3} \quad a = 59°$

$3\cos x° + 5\sin x° = \sqrt{34}\cos(x-59)°$

Specimen Unit assessment B–3(H)

1 $\overrightarrow{AP} = p - a = \begin{pmatrix} 5 \\ -4 \\ -1 \end{pmatrix} - \begin{pmatrix} 3 \\ -2 \\ -2 \end{pmatrix} = \begin{pmatrix} 2 \\ -2 \\ 1 \end{pmatrix}$

$\overrightarrow{PR} = r - p = \begin{pmatrix} 9 \\ -8 \\ 1 \end{pmatrix} - \begin{pmatrix} 5 \\ -4 \\ -1 \end{pmatrix} = \begin{pmatrix} 4 \\ -4 \\ 2 \end{pmatrix} = 2\overrightarrow{AP}$

so $\overrightarrow{AP}$ and $\overrightarrow{PR}$ are parallel and since P is a common point, A, P and R are collinear

2

$b = \tfrac{2}{3}g + \tfrac{1}{3}t = \tfrac{1}{3}(2g + t)$

$= \tfrac{1}{3}\begin{pmatrix} 14 \\ -10 \\ 2 \end{pmatrix} + \begin{pmatrix} 1 \\ 1 \\ 7 \end{pmatrix} = \tfrac{1}{3}\begin{pmatrix} 15 \\ -9 \\ 9 \end{pmatrix} = \begin{pmatrix} 5 \\ -3 \\ 3 \end{pmatrix}$

$B(5, -3, 3)$

3 (a) $\overrightarrow{QP}.\overrightarrow{QR} = \begin{pmatrix} 5 \\ 2 \\ 2 \end{pmatrix}.\begin{pmatrix} 2 \\ 4 \\ 4 \end{pmatrix} = 10 + 8 + 8 = 26$

(b) $\left|\overrightarrow{QP}\right| = \sqrt{25+4+4} = \sqrt{33}$

$\left|\overrightarrow{QR}\right| = \sqrt{4+16+16} = 6$

$\cos PQR = \dfrac{\overrightarrow{QP}.\overrightarrow{QR}}{\left|\overrightarrow{QP}\right|\left|\overrightarrow{QR}\right|} = \dfrac{26}{6\sqrt{33}} = 0.754$

$PQR = 41°$

4 $p.r = \begin{pmatrix} -2 \\ 8 \\ -2 \end{pmatrix}.\begin{pmatrix} -4 \\ -2 \\ -4 \end{pmatrix}$

$= 8 - 16 + 8 = 0$
Hence **p** is perpendicular to **r** since $\cos 90° = 0$

5 $f(x) = 5\sin x + 3\cos x$
$f'(x) = 5\cos x - 3\sin x$

6 (a) $h(x) = (5 + 4x)^3$
$h'(x) = 3(5 + 4x)^2 \times 4$
$= 12(5 + 4x)^2$

(b) $y = \sin 3x + (\cos x)^2$
$\dfrac{dy}{dx} = 3\cos 3x + 2(\cos x)(-\sin x)$
$= 3\cos 3x - 2\sin x \cos x$
$= 3\cos 3x - \sin 2x$

7 (a) $\int_0^2 (x+1)^4\,dx = \left[\dfrac{(x+1)^5}{5}\right]_0^2 = \left(\tfrac{243}{5}\right) - \left(\tfrac{1}{5}\right) = 48\tfrac{2}{5}$

(b) $\int 4\cos x - 2\sin x\,dx = 4\sin x + 2\cos x + C$

8 (a) $\log_{10} 4 + \log_{10} 5 - \log_{10} 2$
$= \log_{10}\left(\dfrac{4 \times 5}{2}\right)$
$= \log_{10} 10 = 1$

(b) $4\log_3 3 - 2\log_3 9$
$= \log_3 3^4 - \log_3 9^2$
$= \log_3 \tfrac{81}{81} = \log_3 1 = 0$

9 (a) $3\log_a x + \log_a 3 = \log_a 2 + \log_a 12$
$\log_a x^3 + \log_a 3 = \log_a (2 \times 12)$
$\log_a 3x^3 = \log_a 24$
$3x^3 = 24$
$x^3 = 8 \quad x = 2$

(b) $e^{2x} = 18 \qquad \ln e^{2x} = \ln 18$
$(\ln e = 1) \quad 2x \ln e = \ln 18$
$2x = \ln 18$
$x = \tfrac{1}{2}\ln 18 = 1.445$

10 $\sqrt{3}\cos x° - \sin x° = k\cos(x+\alpha)°$
$$= k\cos x°\cos\alpha° - k\sin x°\sin\alpha°$$

$\left.\begin{array}{l}\sqrt{3} = k\cos\alpha°\\ 1 = k\sin\alpha°\end{array}\right\}$ $k = \sqrt{3+1} = 2$

$\tan\alpha° = \dfrac{1}{\sqrt{3}}$

S	A
✓	✓ ✓

$\alpha = 30°$

T	C
	✓

$\sqrt{3}\cos x° + \sin x° = 2\cos(x+30)°$

Specimen Course assessment A

Paper I

1 $m_{LN} = \dfrac{-1-(-5)}{-5-3} = -\frac{1}{2}$

$m_{MP} = 2$ M(1, 4)
$y - 4 = 2(x-1)$
$y = 2x + 2$

2 (a) $a = 0.4$; since $-1 < a < 1$ a limit exists

(b) $L = \dfrac{b}{1-a} = \dfrac{-1}{1-0.4} = \dfrac{-1}{0.6} = \dfrac{-5}{3}$

3 (a)

1	2	5	−4	−3
		2	7	3
	2	7	3	**0**

therefore $(x-1)$ is a factor
$(x-1)(2x^2 + 7x + 3)$
$= (x-1)(x+3)(2x+1)$

(b) y-axis $(0, -3)$
x-axis $(1, 0)$, $(-3, 0)$, $(-\frac{1}{2}, 0)$

(c) $f'(x) = 6x^2 + 10x - 4 = 0$ for stationary points
$2(3x^2 + 5x - 2) = 0$
$2(x+2)(3x-1) = 0$
$x = -2, \frac{1}{3}$
$x = -2$, $f(-2) = -8 + 20 + 8 - 3 = 17$
$x = \frac{1}{3}$, $f\left(\frac{1}{3}\right) = \frac{2}{27} + \frac{5}{9} - \frac{4}{3} - 3 = -3\frac{19}{27}$

x	-2^-	-2	-2^+
$f'(x)$	+	0	−
slope	╱	—	╲

maximum turning point at $(-2, 17)$

x	$\frac{1}{3}^-$	$\frac{1}{3}$	$\frac{1}{3}^+$
$f'(x)$	−	0	+
slope	╲	—	╱

minimum turning point $\left(\frac{1}{3}, -3\frac{19}{27}\right)$

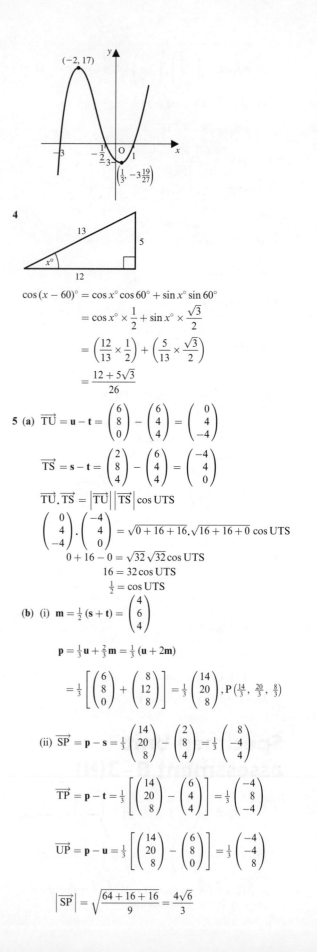

4

$\cos(x-60)° = \cos x°\cos 60° + \sin x°\sin 60°$
$$= \cos x° \times \frac{1}{2} + \sin x° \times \frac{\sqrt{3}}{2}$$
$$= \left(\frac{12}{13} \times \frac{1}{2}\right) + \left(\frac{5}{13} \times \frac{\sqrt{3}}{2}\right)$$
$$= \frac{12 + 5\sqrt{3}}{26}$$

5 (a) $\overrightarrow{TU} = \mathbf{u} - \mathbf{t} = \begin{pmatrix} 6 \\ 8 \\ 0 \end{pmatrix} - \begin{pmatrix} 6 \\ 4 \\ 4 \end{pmatrix} = \begin{pmatrix} 0 \\ 4 \\ -4 \end{pmatrix}$

$\overrightarrow{TS} = \mathbf{s} - \mathbf{t} = \begin{pmatrix} 2 \\ 8 \\ 4 \end{pmatrix} - \begin{pmatrix} 6 \\ 4 \\ 4 \end{pmatrix} = \begin{pmatrix} -4 \\ 4 \\ 0 \end{pmatrix}$

$\overrightarrow{TU}.\overrightarrow{TS} = \left|\overrightarrow{TU}\right|\left|\overrightarrow{TS}\right|\cos UTS$

$\begin{pmatrix} 0 \\ 4 \\ -4 \end{pmatrix}.\begin{pmatrix} -4 \\ 4 \\ 0 \end{pmatrix} = \sqrt{0+16+16}.\sqrt{16+16+0}\cos UTS$

$0 + 16 - 0 = \sqrt{32}\sqrt{32}\cos UTS$
$16 = 32\cos UTS$
$\frac{1}{2} = \cos UTS$

(b) (i) $\mathbf{m} = \frac{1}{2}(\mathbf{s}+\mathbf{t}) = \begin{pmatrix} 4 \\ 6 \\ 4 \end{pmatrix}$

$\mathbf{p} = \frac{1}{3}\mathbf{u} + \frac{2}{3}\mathbf{m} = \frac{1}{3}(\mathbf{u}+2\mathbf{m})$

$= \frac{1}{3}\left[\begin{pmatrix} 6 \\ 8 \\ 0 \end{pmatrix} + \begin{pmatrix} 8 \\ 12 \\ 8 \end{pmatrix}\right] = \frac{1}{3}\begin{pmatrix} 14 \\ 20 \\ 8 \end{pmatrix}$, $P\left(\frac{14}{3}, \frac{20}{3}, \frac{8}{3}\right)$

(ii) $\overrightarrow{SP} = \mathbf{p} - \mathbf{s} = \frac{1}{3}\begin{pmatrix} 14 \\ 20 \\ 8 \end{pmatrix} - \begin{pmatrix} 2 \\ 8 \\ 4 \end{pmatrix} = \frac{1}{3}\begin{pmatrix} 8 \\ -4 \\ 4 \end{pmatrix}$

$\overrightarrow{TP} = \mathbf{p} - \mathbf{t} = \frac{1}{3}\left[\begin{pmatrix} 14 \\ 20 \\ 8 \end{pmatrix} - \begin{pmatrix} 6 \\ 4 \\ 4 \end{pmatrix}\right] = \frac{1}{3}\begin{pmatrix} -4 \\ 8 \\ -4 \end{pmatrix}$

$\overrightarrow{UP} = \mathbf{p} - \mathbf{u} = \frac{1}{3}\left[\begin{pmatrix} 14 \\ 20 \\ 8 \end{pmatrix} - \begin{pmatrix} 6 \\ 8 \\ 0 \end{pmatrix}\right] = \frac{1}{3}\begin{pmatrix} -4 \\ -4 \\ 8 \end{pmatrix}$

$\left|\overrightarrow{SP}\right| = \sqrt{\dfrac{64+16+16}{9}} = \dfrac{4\sqrt{6}}{3}$

$$\left|\overrightarrow{TP}\right| = \sqrt{\frac{16 + 64 + 16}{9}} = \frac{4\sqrt{6}}{3}$$

$$\left|\overrightarrow{UP}\right| = \sqrt{\frac{16 + 16 + 64}{9}} = \frac{4\sqrt{6}}{3}$$

Hence S, T and U are equidistant from P

6 $C_1 = (6, 3), r_1 = \sqrt{36 + 9 - 36} = 3$
$C_2 = (6 + 4, 3) = (10, 3), r_2 = 4 - 3 = 1$
equation of smaller circle is $(x - 10)^2 + (y - 3)^2 = 1$
$$x^2 + y^2 - 20x - 6y + 108 = 0$$

7 $\displaystyle\int_{-\sqrt{2}}^{0} t^3 - 2t\,dt$

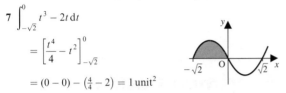

$$= \left[\frac{t^4}{4} - t^2\right]_{-\sqrt{2}}^{0}$$

$$= (0 - 0) - \left(\tfrac{4}{4} - 2\right) = 1\,\text{unit}^2$$

8 period $= 360°$ amplitude $= 3$ horizontal shift $= 45°$ left

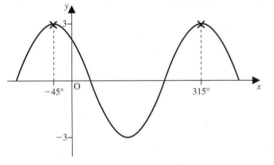

9 $y = (2 - \sin x)^{\frac{1}{2}}$

$$\frac{dy}{dx} = \frac{1}{2}(2 - \sin x)^{-\frac{1}{2}} \times (-\cos x)$$

$$= \frac{-\cos x}{2\sqrt{2 - \sin x}}$$

10 $\left.\begin{array}{l} y = 6 \\ y = 3\log_4(3x + 4) \end{array}\right\}$ intersect when

$$3\log_4(3x + 4) = 6$$
$$\log_4(3x + 4) = 2$$
$$3x + 4 = 4^2$$
$$3x + 4 = 16$$
$$3x = 12$$
$$x = 4$$

Specimen Course assessment A

Paper II

1 $m_{SR} = m_{PQ} = \dfrac{2 - 1}{6 - (-1)} = \dfrac{1}{7}$

R$(7, -4)$ $m = \frac{1}{7}$
$y + 4 = \frac{1}{7}(x - 7)$
$7y + 28 = x - 7$
$x - 7y = 35$

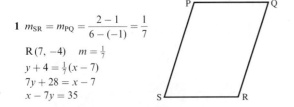

2 $B_{n+1} = 0.3\,B_n + 350$
$a = 0.3$, so since $-1 < a < 1$, a limit exists
$$L_B = \frac{b}{1 - a} = \frac{350}{1 - 0.3} = 500 \text{ pests}$$
$N_{n+1} = 0.1\,N_n + 400$
$a = 0.1$, so since $-1 < a < 1$, a limit exists
$$L_N = \frac{b}{1 - a} = \frac{400}{1 - 0.1} = 444 \text{ pests}$$
since $L_B > L_N$, Nobug is more effective in the long term than Bugoff

3 **(a)** $f(x) = 3x^2 + 30x + 73$
$= 3(x^2 + 10x) + 73$
$= 3(x^2 + 10x + 25) + 73 - 75$
$= 3(x + 5)^2 - 2$

  (b) Minimum turning point at $(-5, -2)$

4 **(a)** $\dfrac{dy}{dx} = 3x^2 - 2x - 4$
at $x = 1$, $m = 3 - 2 - 4 = -3$ A$(1, -3)$
$y + 3 = -3(x - 1)$
$y + 3x = 0$

  (b) $\left.\begin{array}{l} y + 3x = 0 \\ y = x^3 - x^2 - 4x + 1 \end{array}\right\}$ intersect when
$x^3 - x^2 - 4x + 1 = -3x$
$x^3 - x^2 - x + 1 = 0$

$$\begin{array}{c|cccc} 1 & 1 & -1 & -1 & 1 \\ & & 1 & 0 & -1 \\ \hline & 1 & 0 & -1 & \mathbf{0} \end{array}$$

$(x - 1)(x^2 - 1) = 0$
$(x - 1)(x - 1)(x + 1) = 0$
$x = -1$ or $x = 1$
when $x = -1$, $y = -1 - 1 + 4 + 1 = 3$, B$(-1, 3)$

  (c) $A = \displaystyle\int_{-1}^{1} (x^3 - x^2 - 4x + 1) - (-3x)\,dx$

$$= \int_{-1}^{1} x^3 - x^2 - x + 1\,dx$$

$$= \left[\frac{x^4}{4} - \frac{x^3}{3} - \frac{x^2}{2} + x\right]_{-1}^{1}$$

$$= \left(\tfrac{1}{4} - \tfrac{1}{3} - \tfrac{1}{2} + 1\right) - \left(\tfrac{1}{4} + \tfrac{1}{3} - \tfrac{1}{2} - 1\right)$$

$$= \tfrac{4}{3}\,\text{units}^2$$

5 **(a)** $C_1 = (1, 3), r_1 = \sqrt{1 + 9 + 26} = 6$
$C_2 = (1, 3), r_2 = 7 - 3 = 4$
$(x - 1)^2 + (y - 3)^2 = 4^2$
$x^2 + y^2 - 2x - 6y - 6 = 0$

  (b) $r > 6$
$g^2 + f^2 - c > 36$
$1 + 9 - c > 36$
$-26 > c$

6 **(a)** (i) $\mathbf{b}.\mathbf{c} = |\mathbf{b}|\,|\mathbf{c}|\cos 60° = 5 \times 5 \times \tfrac{1}{2} = 12\tfrac{1}{2}$
    (ii) $\mathbf{b}.(\mathbf{c} + \mathbf{a}) = \mathbf{b}.\mathbf{c} + \mathbf{b}.\mathbf{a}$
$= 12\tfrac{1}{2} + 5 \times 5\cos 60°$
$= 12\tfrac{1}{2} + 12\tfrac{1}{2} = 25$

  (b) (i) $\overrightarrow{IV} = \overrightarrow{IF} + \overrightarrow{FG} + \overrightarrow{GV}$
$= -\mathbf{a} - \mathbf{c} + \mathbf{b} = \mathbf{b} - \mathbf{a} - \mathbf{c}$
    (ii) $\overrightarrow{GV}.\overrightarrow{IV} = \mathbf{b}(\mathbf{b} - \mathbf{a} - \mathbf{c})$
$= \mathbf{b}.\mathbf{b} - \mathbf{b}.\mathbf{a} - \mathbf{b}.\mathbf{a}$
$= |\mathbf{b}|\,|\mathbf{b}|\cos 0° - 12\tfrac{1}{2} - 12\tfrac{1}{2}$
$= 5 \times 5 \times 1 - 25$
$= 25 - 25 = 0$
hence GV is perpendicular to IV

7 (a) $3\sin x° + 5\cos x° = k\cos x°\cos α° + k\sin x°\sin α°$

$\left.\begin{array}{l}3 = k\sin α° \\ 5 = k\cos α°\end{array}\right\}$ $k = \sqrt{3^2 + 5^2} = \sqrt{34}$

$\tan α° = \frac{3}{5}, α = 31°$

$f(x) = \sqrt{34}\cos(x - 31)°$

(b) $\sqrt{34}\cos(x - 31)° = 0.2$

$\cos(x - 31)° = 0.034$

$x° - 31 = 88, 272$

$x = 119°, 303°$

S	A
	✓
T	C ✓

(c) $3\sin x° + 5\cos x° = 0$

$\sqrt{34}\cos(x - 31)° = 0$

$x° - 31 = 90$

$x = 121°$

8 (a) $\text{LHS} = 2\cos 2x° + 3\sin^2 x°$

$= 2(2\cos^2 x - 1)° + 3\sin^2 x°$

$= 4\cos^2 x° - 2 + 3\sin^2 x°$

$= 3(\sin^2 x° + \cos^2 x°) + \cos^2 x° - 2$

$= 3 + \cos^2 x° - 2$

$= 1 + \cos^2 x°$

$= \text{RHS}$

(b) (i) $2\cos 2x° + 3\sin^2 x° = 3\cos^2 x°$

$1 + \cos^2 x° = 3\cos^2 x°$

$1 = 2\cos^2 x°$

$\frac{1}{2} = \cos^2 x°$

$\pm\frac{1}{\sqrt{2}} = \cos x°$

(ii) For $0 \leqslant x < 90$, $x = 45°$

9 $(x - 4)(x - k) = -9$

$x^2 - 4x - kx + 4k = -9$

$x^2 - (4 + k)x + (4k + 9) = 0$

for equal roots, $b^2 - 4ac = 0$

$16 + 8k + k^2 - 16k - 36 = 0$

$k^2 - 8k - 20 = 0$

$(k - 10)(k + 2) = 0$

$k = 10, -2$

10 (a) (i) $\text{Perimeter} = 4s + 2t + \frac{1}{2}C$

$150 = 4s + 2t + \frac{1}{2}(\pi \times 4s)$

$150 - 4s - 2\pi s = 2t$

$75 - 2s - \pi s = t$

(ii) $A = 4st + \frac{1}{2}\pi(2s)^2$

$A = 4s(75 - 2s - \pi s) + 2\pi s^2$

$A = 300s - 8s^2 - 2\pi s^2$

(b) (i) $\dfrac{\mathrm{d}A}{\mathrm{d}s} = 300 - 16s - 4\pi s = 0$

$300 = (16 + 4\pi)s$

$s = \dfrac{300}{16 + 4\pi} = \dfrac{75}{4 + \pi} = 10.5\,\text{m}$

s	10.5^-	10.5	10.5^+
$\dfrac{\mathrm{d}A}{\mathrm{d}s}$	$+$	0	$-$
slope	╱	—	╲

Hence at $s = 10.5$, area is a maximum

(ii) When $s = 10.5$, $A = 300 \times 10.5 - (8 + 2\pi)10.5^2$

$A = 1575.3\,\text{m}^2$

11 (a) $m = \dfrac{5.093 - 2.747}{2.219 - 0.916} = 1.8$

$Y = 1.8X + c$

substituting $(0.916, 2.747)$ gives

$2.747 = 1.8 \times 0.916 + c$

$1.1 = c$

$Y = 1.8X + 1.1$

(b) $\ln y = 1.8\ln x + 1.1$

$b = 1.8, c = \ln a$

$\ln a = 1.1$

$a = 3$

$y = 3x^{1.8}$

Specimen Course assessment B
Paper I

1 (a)

4	2	15	-104	48
		8	92	-48
	2	23	-12	**0**

therefore $x = 4$ is a root of the equation

(b) $(x - 4)(2x^2 + 23x - 12) = (x - 4)(2x - 1)(x + 12)$

2 (a) $m_{PQ} = \frac{2}{6} = \frac{1}{3}$

equation of PQ is $y - 5 = \frac{1}{3}(x + 4)$

$x - 3y + 19 = 0$

(b) $m_{perp} = -3$

mid-point of PQ is $(-1, 6)$

equation of perpendicular bisector is

$y - 6 = -3(x + 1)$

$3x + y = 3$

3 (a)

$y = 3x - 1$

$y = 3 \times 3 - 1$

$= 8$

$y = 3 \times 6 + 1$

$= 17$

$A = (3 \times 8) + \frac{1}{2}(3 \times 9)$

$= 37\frac{1}{2}\,\text{units}^2$

(b) $A = \displaystyle\int_3^6 (3x - 1)\,\mathrm{d}x$

(c) $\displaystyle\int_3^6 (3x - 1)\,\mathrm{d}x = \left[\frac{3}{2}x^2 - x\right]_3^6$

$= \left(\frac{3 \times 36}{2} - 6\right) - \left(\frac{3 \times 9}{2} - 3\right)$

$= 37\frac{1}{2}$

4 $\dfrac{dy}{dx} = 6x + 2$

at A$(-3, 9)$ $\dfrac{dy}{dx} = -16$

equation of tangent at A is $y - 9 = -16(x + 3)$

$$16x + y = -39$$

5 (a)

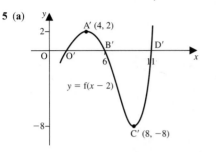

(b)

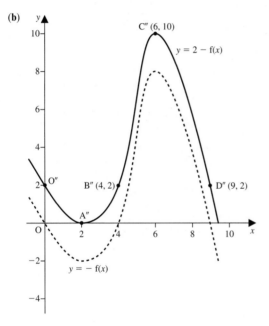

6 $\dfrac{dy}{dx} = x^3 + 2x^{-2} - \dfrac{1}{3}$

$y = \dfrac{x^4}{4} + \dfrac{2x^{-1}}{-1} - \dfrac{1}{3}x + C$

$y = \dfrac{1}{4}x^4 - \dfrac{2}{x} - \dfrac{1}{3}x + C$

when $x = -1$

$y = \dfrac{1}{4} + 2 + \dfrac{1}{3} + C = 2$

$C = \dfrac{24}{12} - \dfrac{3}{12} - \dfrac{24}{12} - \dfrac{4}{12}$

$C = -\dfrac{7}{12}$

$y = \dfrac{1}{4}x^4 - \dfrac{1}{3}x - \dfrac{2}{x} - \dfrac{7}{12}$

7

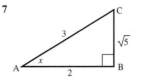

$\sin x = \dfrac{\sqrt{5}}{3}$

$\cos x = \dfrac{2}{3}$

$\sin 2x = 2 \sin x \cos x$

$= 2 \times \dfrac{\sqrt{5}}{3} \times \dfrac{2}{3}$

$= \dfrac{4\sqrt{5}}{9}$

8 $p \cos 4x° = \dfrac{p}{2}$

$\cos 4x° = \tfrac{1}{2}$

$4x° = 60$ or 300

$x = 15°$ or $75°$

Hence x coordinates of M and N are 15 and 75 respectively.

9 $y = \log_b x$ has moved 2 units horizontally to the left to give $y = \log_b (x + a)$, $a = 2$
The point (7, 1) lies on the graph of $y = \log_b x$, $b = 7$

10 $y = 4x^3 - x^4$

$\dfrac{dy}{dx} = 12x^2 - 4x^3$

at stationary points

$12x^2 - 4x^3 = 0$

$4x^2(3 - x) = 0$

$x = 0$ or $x = 3$

Stationary values are 0 and 27

x	0^-	0	0^+	27^-	27	27^+
$\dfrac{dy}{dx}$	+	0	+	+	0	−
slope						
nature		point of inflexion			maximum turning point	

(0, 0) is a point of inflexion
(3, 27) is a maximum turning point

11 $\displaystyle\int \left(\dfrac{x^2 + 3}{x^{\frac{3}{2}}}\right) dx = \int \left(x^{\frac{1}{2}} + 3x^{-\frac{3}{2}}\right) dx$

$= \dfrac{x^{\frac{3}{2}}}{\frac{3}{2}} + \dfrac{3x^{-\frac{1}{2}}}{-\frac{1}{2}} + C$

$= \dfrac{2}{3}x^{\frac{3}{2}} - 6x^{-\frac{1}{2}} + C$

12 $u_{n+1} = 0.1u_n + p$

$$L = \frac{p}{1 - 0.1} = \frac{p}{0.9}$$

$v_{n+1} = 0.7v_n + q$

$$L = \frac{q}{1 - 0.7} = \frac{q}{0.3}$$

$$\frac{p}{0.9} = \frac{q}{0.3}$$

$$p = \frac{0.9}{0.3}q$$

$$p = 3q$$

Specimen Course assessment B

Paper II

1

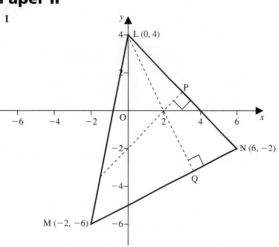

(a) $m_{MN} = \frac{4}{8} = \frac{1}{2}$

$m_{alt} = -2$

equation of altitude LQ is $y - 4 = -2(x - 0)$
$$y = -2x + 4$$

(b) $m_{LN} = -\frac{6}{6} = -1$

$m_{perp} = 1$

mid-point P is (3, 1)

equation of perpendicular bisector is
$$y - 1 = 1(x - 3)$$
$$y = x - 2$$

(c) Point of intersection where $x - 2 = -2x + 4$
$$3x = 6$$
$$x = 2$$
$$y = 0$$

point is (2, 0)

2 (a) C is (4, 2)

$$m_{CP} = \frac{2}{-6} = \frac{-1}{3}$$

$m_{PQ} = 3$

equation of tan PQ is
$$y - 4 = 3(x + 2)$$
$$y = 3x + 10$$

(b) When $x = 0$, $y = 3 \times 0 + 10$
$$y = 10$$

Q is (0, 10)

(c) radius CQ $= \sqrt{(-4)^2 + 8^2}$
$$= \sqrt{80}$$

equation of circle is
$$(x - 4)^2 + (y - 2)^2 = 80$$
$$x^2 - 8x + 16 + y^2 - 4y + 4 = 80$$
$$x^2 + y^2 - 8x - 4y - 60 = 0$$

circle meets $y = 3x + 10$ where
$$x^2 + (3x + 10)^2 - 8x - 4(3x + 10) - 60 = 0$$
$$x^2 + 9x^2 + 60x + 100 - 8x - 12x - 40 - 60 = 0$$
$$10x^2 + 40x = 0$$
$$10x(x + 4) = 0$$
$$x = 0 \text{ or } x = -4$$

Q(0, 10)   R(−4, −2)

3

```
         2         ⋮      1
R ———————————— Q ———————— S
(6, 5, −1)      (4, 3, 1)
```

(a) S(3, 2, 2)

(b) P(1, 6, 4)

$$\overrightarrow{SP} = \begin{pmatrix} -2 \\ 4 \\ 2 \end{pmatrix} \qquad \overrightarrow{SQ} = \begin{pmatrix} 1 \\ 1 \\ -1 \end{pmatrix}$$

$\overrightarrow{SP} \cdot \overrightarrow{SQ} = -2 + 4 - 2 = 0$

hence PS is an altitude

4 (a) When $y = 0$, $7 - 6x - x^2 = 0$
$$(7 + x)(1 - x) = 0$$
$$x = -7 \text{ or } x = 1$$

A is the point (−7, 0)

(b) $m_{AB} = \frac{7}{7} = 1$

equation of AB is $y = x + 7$

(c) $A = \displaystyle\int_{-7}^{0} (7 - 6x - x^2) - (x + 7)\,dx$

$$= \int_{-7}^{0} (-7x - x^2)\,dx$$

$$= \left[\frac{-7x^2}{2} - \frac{x^3}{3} \right]_{-7}^{0}$$

$$= 0 - \left(-\frac{343}{2} + \frac{343}{3} \right)$$

$$= 57\frac{1}{6} \text{ units}^2$$

5 (a)
2 pm $u_0 = 40$
3 pm $u_1 = 0.85 \times 40$
4 pm $u_2 = 0.85^2 \times 40$
5 pm $u_3 = 0.85^3 \times 40$
$= 24.6$ units

(b) $u_{n+1} = au_n + b$
$u_{n+1} = 0.85^3 u_n + 40$
a limit exists since $0.85^3 < 1$

$$L = \frac{b}{1 - a} = \frac{40}{1 - 0.85^3}$$
$$= 103.7 \text{ units}$$

therefore the treatment is not safe

6 (a) $f(g(x)) = f(x + 1)$
$$= (x + 1)^3 + (x + 1)^2 - 6(x + 1)$$
$$= x^3 + 3x^2 + 3x + 1 + x^2 + 2x + 1 - 6x - 6$$
$$= x^3 + 4x^2 - x - 4$$

(b)

1	1	4	−1	−4
		1	5	4
	1	5	4	0

$f(g(x)) = (x-1)(x^2 + 5x + 4)$
$\qquad\quad = (x-1)(x+1)(x+4)$

(c) $k(x) = \dfrac{1}{(x-1)(x+1)(x+4)}$

$k(x)$ is not defined for $x = 1$, $x = -1$ and $x = -4$

7 (a) $AD^2 = OA^2 + OD^2 - 2OA.OD\cos(180 - \theta)°$
$\qquad\quad = r^2 + OD^2 - 2.r.OD.(-\cos\theta)°$
$\qquad\quad = r^2 + OD^2 + 2r.OD.\cos\theta°$

$\cos\theta° = \dfrac{OD}{OB}$

$OD = OB\cos\theta°$
$\qquad = r\cos\theta°$
$OD^2 = r^2\cos^2\theta°$
$AD^2 = r^2 + r^2\cos^2\theta° + 2r.r\cos\theta°.\cos\theta°$
$\qquad\quad = r^2 + r^2\cos^2\theta° + 2r^2\cos^2\theta°$
$\qquad\quad = r^2 + 3r^2\cos^2\theta°$
$\qquad\quad = r^2(1 + 3\cos^2\theta°)$

(b) If BD bisects angle OBS then triangle OBS is equilateral
$\theta = 60°$

$\cos\theta = \frac{1}{2}$
$AD^2 = r^2\left(1 + 3 \times \left(\frac{1}{2}\right)^2\right)$
$\qquad\quad = r^2 \times \frac{7}{4}$
$AD = \dfrac{r}{2}\sqrt{7}$

8 (a) $m = m_0e^{-0.03t}$

$m = 400e^{-0.15}$ when $t = 5$
mass after 5 years $= 344.3\,g$

(b) $\quad 200 = 400\,e^{-0.03t}$
$e^{-0.03t} = \frac{1}{2}$
$\ln e^{-0.03t} = \ln 0.5$
$-0.03t = -0.693$
$\qquad t = 23.1$ years

9 (a) $24\cos x° - 7\sin x°$
$= k\sin(x - \alpha)°$
$= k(\sin x°\cos\alpha° - \cos x°\sin\alpha°)$
$= k\sin x°\cos\alpha° - k\cos x°\sin\alpha°$
so $-7\sin x° + 24\cos x°$
$= k\cos\alpha°\sin x° - k\sin\alpha°\cos x°$
hence $k\cos\alpha° = -7$
$\qquad k\sin\alpha° = -24$

$k = \sqrt{(-7)^2 + (-24)^2} = \sqrt{625} = 25$

$\tan\alpha° = \dfrac{-24}{-7}$

α is in the third quadrant, therefore $\alpha = 253.7°$
$24\cos x° - 7\sin x° = 25\sin(x - 253.7)°$

(b) $25\sin(x - 253.7)° = 20$

$\sin(x - 253.7)° = \frac{20}{25} = 0.8$

$(x - 253.7) = 53.1$ or 126.9
$x = 306.8$

10 (a) $\quad y = x^2 + px + q$
$\qquad -6 = (-1)^2 - p + q$
$\qquad p - q = 7$

(b) $\dfrac{dy}{dx} = 2x + p$

$2x + p = 1$
At A, when $x = -1$, $2 \times (-1) + p = 1$
$p = 3$
when $p = 3$, $3 - q = 7$
$\qquad\qquad q = -4$
equation of parabola is $y = x^2 + 3x - 4$

(c) $x^2 + 3x - 4 = 0$
$b^2 - 4ac = 9 + 16 = 25$
the graph crosses the x-axis at points with x-coordinates that are real and rational

11 $C = 250r + \dfrac{27}{r^2}$

$C(r) = 250r + 27r^{-2}$
$C'(r) = 250 - 54r^{-3}$
at stationary points $C'(r) = 0$

$250 - \dfrac{54}{r^3} = 0$
$\dfrac{54}{r^3} = 250$
$r^3 = \dfrac{54}{250}$
$r = 0.6$

r	0.6^-	0.6	0.6^+
$C'(r)$	−	0	+
slope	╲	──	╱
nature		minimum turning point	

hence cost is a minimum when $r = 0.6\,m$
minimum cost $= C(0.6)$
$\qquad\qquad\qquad = 250 \times 0.6 + \frac{27}{0.6^2}$
$\qquad\qquad\qquad = £225$ million

Heinemann Educational Publishers,
a division of Heinemann Publishers (Oxford) Ltd,
Halley Court, Jordan Hill, Oxford, OX2 8EJ

OXFORD BLANTYRE MELBOURNE AUCKLAND IBADAN
GABORONE PORTSMOUTH NH (USA) CHICAGO JOHANNESBURG

© Scottish Secondary Mathematics Group 1999

First published 1999

02
10 9 8 7 6 5 4

ISBN 0 435 516205

Original design by Wendi Watson
Original cover design by Aricot Vert
Cover photograph: Science Photo Library
Typeset and illustrated by TechSet Ltd, Gateshead, Tyne and Wear
Printed in Great Britain by The Bath Press, Bath

Acknowledgements
The publisher's and authors' thanks are due to the Scottish Examination Board
(SEB) for permission to reproduce questions from past Higher Grade Mathematics
Examination papers. These are marked [Higher].
The answers have been provided by the authors and are not the responsibility of the
examining board.
Specimen assessments are based on all information currently available.

With many thanks to A. McKee for his contribution to the work of the author team.

Higher Maths on the net
Become a registered user to obtain updates from our website at
www.heinemann.co.uk/Higher_Mathematics.

Author team:
John B. Dalton
Carole L. Ford
James K. Pennel
Thomas J. Sanaghan

Publishing team:
Editorial
Philip Ellaway
Shaheen Hassan
Lesley Montford

Design
Phil Richards
Colette Jacquelin
Mags Robertson

Production
Jo Morgan

Cover picture: **vectors in space**

High above the Earth a space shuttle orbits. The diagram shows its velocity
resolved into two components – one at a tangent to the orbit, the other
towards the centre of the Earth.

There is more about components of vectors in Chapter 13.

Tel:01865 888058 email:info.he@heinemann.co.uk